Collins Advanced Modular Sciences

Particles, Principles and Possibilities

WITHDRAWN

David Brodie

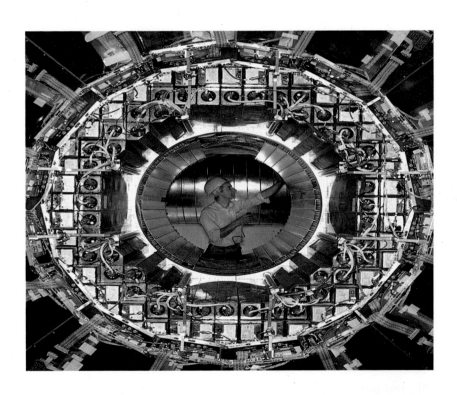

Series Editor: Mike Coles

Collins Educational

An Imprint of HarperCollins*Publishers*

Northern
Modular Science Scheme

Published by Collins Educational
An imprint of HarperCollins*Publishers* Ltd
77–85 Fulham Palace Road
Hammersmith
London
W6 8JB

First published 1996

ISBN 0 00 322390 6

British Library Cataloguing in Publication Data
A catalogue record for this book is available from the British Library.

Edited by Alan Trewartha and Jenny Hughes.

Book design by Ewing Paddock at PearTree Design.

Design and layout by Derek Lee.

Illustrations by Mainline Design, Peter Harper and Alan Trewartha.

Picture research by Caroline Thompson and Dee Robinson.

Production by Mandy Inness.

Printed and bound by Edinburgh Press Ltd, Scotland

Contents

	To the student	5
1	Modelling the nucleus	6
2	Accelerating costs	16
3	Strangeness and charm in California	25
4	Radioactive Earth	36
5	Decaying atoms, preserving food	44
6	A nuclear commitment	56
7	The electronic era	70
8	Seen in a different light	79
9	Microworlds	91
10	Steam-driven empires	99
11	Cold new world	106
12	Einstein's time	116
	Data section	129
	Answers to questions	134
	Glossary	143
	Biographical glossary	147
	Index	150

Acknowledgements

Text and diagrams reproduced by kind permission of:

Faber and Faber Ltd
New Scientist, IPC Magazines
Isotron plc, Swindon

Every effort has been made to contact the holders of copyright material, but if any have been inadvertently overlooked the publishers will be pleased to make the necessary arrangements at the first opportunity.

Photographs
The publishers would like to thank the following for permission to reproduce photographs (T = Top, B = Bottom, C = Centre, L= Left, R = Right):

AEA Technology 61;
Professor J F Allen 106BR, 114T;
Ancient Art and Architecture 31R;
BT Corporate Picture Library: a BT Photograph 70TL, 70BR;
John Birdsall Photography 44TR&CR, 86B;
Birmingham International Airport Ltd 106BC;
California Institute of Technology 26C, 29BL;
CERN Photo 24BL;
Camera Obscura, Edinburgh 80R;
Casio Electronics Co Ltd 88;
Corbis 25B;
Corbis/Everett 6TR;
FSP/Gamma 16TR (Brad Markel/Liaison), 63 (Ch. Vioujaro);
John Frost Historical News Service 56L;
Ronald Grant Archive 25T, 116T;
Hulton Getty Picture Collection Ltd 70TR&BC, 79TL, 85TR,
Mark Jordan 19CL, 41L, 48, 106CL;
Kansas Collection, Kansas University, USA 99;
Kobal Collection 17R;

Paramount (courtesy Kobal) 26L;
Andrew Lambert 8, 10, 14, 83, 93, 94;
Landform Slides 39T;
Peter Newark's Pictures 102, 105;
Popperfoto 16CR, 65R;
Reuters/Popperfoto 56TL;
Rex Features 31L, 65L, 78, 86C, 110B;
Science Photo Library 1, 6TL, 16CL, 16C, 17L, 18, 22, 19C, 21, 23, 24BC, 25R, 26R, 28, 29TL&CR, 30, 36BL, 37, 39B, 40, 41R, 51, 53, 58, 60, 62, 64, 66, 67, 79TR&BR, 81B, 82, 85CL, 91, 97, 110TL, 114BL, 115, 116C, 125;
Science Museum/Science & Society Picture Library 70BL, 80L, 81T, 100;
SHOUT Pictures 106TL, 108, 111;
Sony 79BL;
Sygma/Franco Origlia 36T;
Tony Stone Images 44TL, 50, 71, 106TR, 120;
University of Cambridge, Cavendish Laboratory 16TL;

Cover photograph supplied by Science Photo Library.

To the student

This book aims to make your study of advanced science successful and interesting. The authors have made sure that the ideas you need to understand are covered in a clear and straightforward way. The book is designed to be a study of scientific ideas as well as a reference text when needed. Science is constantly evolving and, wherever possible, modern issues and problems have been used to make your study interesting and to encourage you to continue studying science after your current course is complete.

Working on your own

Studying on your own is often difficult and sometimes textbooks give you the impression that you have to be an expert in the subject before you can read the book. I hope you find that this book is not like that. The authors have carefully built up ideas, so that when you are working on your own there is less chance of you becoming lost in the text and frustrated with the subject.

Don't try to achieve too much in one reading session. Science is complex and some demanding ideas need to be supported with a lot of facts. Trying to take in too much at one time can make you lose sight of the most important ideas – all you see is a mass of information. Use the learning objectives to select one idea to study in a particular session.

Chapter design

Each chapter starts by showing how the science you will learn is applied somewhere in the world. Next come learning objectives which tell you exactly what you should learn as you read the chapter. These are written in a way which spells out what you will be able to do with your new knowledge, rather like a checklist – they could be very helpful when you revise your work. At certain points in the chapters you will find key ideas listed. These are checks for you to use, to make sure that you have grasped these ideas. Words written in **bold type** appear in the glossary at the end of the book. If you don't know the meaning of one of these words check it out immediately – don't persevere, hoping all will become clear.

The questions in the text are there for you to check you have understood what is being explained. These are all short – longer questions are included in a support pack which goes with this book. The questions are straightforward in style – there are no trick questions. Don't be tempted to pass over these questions, they will give you new insights into the work which you may not have seen. Answers to questions are given in the back of the book.

Good luck with your studies. I hope you find the book an interesting read.

Mike Coles, Series Editor
University of London Institute of Education, June 1995

Modelling the nucleus

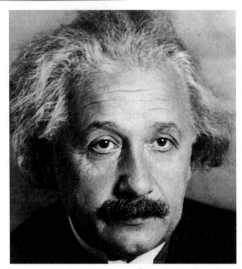

'Imagination is more important than knowledge.'

'Commonsense is nothing more than a deposit of prejudices laid down by the mind before you reach eighteen.'

Albert Einstein

At the end of the 19th century, many scientists were proclaiming that there was little left to do in the field of physics – just some tidying up. One of the phenomena that refused to be tidied up was radioactivity. Investigating this phenomenon opened up the realm of the atom, and led to the creation of nuclear models of the atom, wave–particle duality and 'fundamental particles'. Rather than creaking to a halt, physics was to be transformed.

Enormous changes swept through physics in the 20th century. From relativity and radioactivity to quantum theory and quarks – all these ideas overturned previous ideas and replaced them with new, and occasionally crazy, views of the way matter and energy behave. So be prepared – the science in this book will be unexpected, probably surprising and certainly unfinished.

It wasn't just physics that changed in the 20th century. The public attitude to science and technology has dramatically shifted more than once.

Table 1 Revolutionary physics in the 20th century	
(radioactivity	1896)
relativity	1905
quantum theory	1906
nucleus	1911
transmutation of elements	1919
fission	1938
nuclear power	1942
quarks	1964

1.1 Learning objectives

After working through this chapter, you should be able to:

- **explain** why bombarding nuclei with alpha particles can give an approximate measurement of nuclear size;

- **explain** why electron diffraction provides a more accurate measurement of nuclear size;

- **state** the relationship between nuclear radius and nucleon number;

- **explain** the constant density of nuclei in terms of nucleon behaviour;

- **describe** the action of electric and strong nuclear forces between nucleons;

- **interpret** force–distance graphs for neutrons and protons;

- **relate** force–distance graphs to corresponding energy–distance graphs;

- **list** the strengths and weaknesses of the liquid drop model of a nucleus.

1.2 Target practice

Fig. 1 Geiger and Marsden's experimental set-up

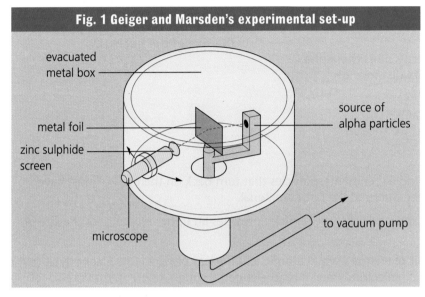

- evacuated metal box
- source of alpha particles
- metal foil
- zinc sulphide screen
- microscope
- to vacuum pump

Fig. 2 Alpha particle scattering

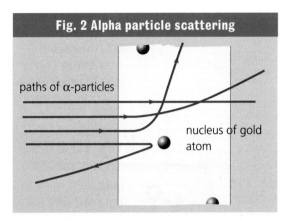

paths of α-particles

nucleus of gold atom

The scattering of **alpha particles** by gold leaf was the first evidence for the existence of the atomic nucleus (see Fig. 1, Fig. 2 and *Physics Core* book, p. 137). But the study of alpha particle scattering can tell us much more. It can give us an upper estimate for the size of a nucleus.

A small number of alpha particles are found to 'bounce back' from the gold leaf atoms. Nuclei are very small compared with the space between them, so most alpha particles do not pass close enough to a nucleus to be significantly deflected. If an alpha particle does directly approach a gold nucleus, it does not hit the nucleus, but slows down instead. It slows down because of the electrical repulsion between the nucleus and the alpha particle (Fig. 3). The

particle turns back on itself and accelerates away from the nucleus. If we can find out how close these 'direct-hit' particles get to the nucleus, we can take this distance of closest approach as an upper estimate for the size of a gold nucleus.

The energy of sub-atomic particles is not usually measured in joules, as this is a very large unit for such small particles. Physicists find it much more convenient to use the **electronvolt** (eV). This is the kinetic energy transferred to a particle with the charge of an electron when it is accelerated through a potential difference of one volt (Fig. 4). One eV is equivalent to 1.6×10^{-19} J.

Fig. 4 Accelerating charged particles at a target

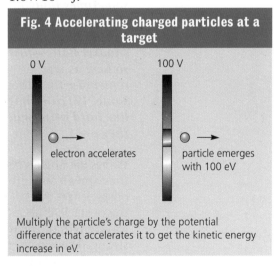

0 V

100 V

electron accelerates

particle emerges with 100 eV

Multiply the particle's charge by the potential difference that accelerates it to get the kinetic energy increase in eV.

These experiments, bombarding atoms with alpha particles, indicated that the atom had a nucleus *and* that it was a tiny fraction of the whole atom. The nuclear model of the atom was born.

Fig. 3 An alpha particle near a gold nucleus

gold, $q = +80e$ α-particle, $q = +4e$ 1 fm $= 10^{-15}$ m

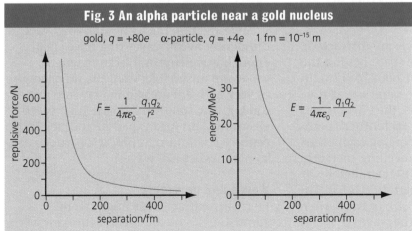

$$F = \frac{1}{4\pi\varepsilon_0}\frac{q_1 q_2}{r^2}$$

repulsive force/N vs separation/fm

$$E = \frac{1}{4\pi\varepsilon_0}\frac{q_1 q_2}{r}$$

energy/MeV vs separation/fm

1 An alpha particle with energy 10 MeV approaches a gold nucleus directly.

   a What type of energy does the alpha particle have before it nears the nucleus?

   b What sort of energy does the alpha particle have at its distance of closest approach?

   c Use the potential energy–distance graph in Fig. 3 to estimate the distance of closest approach for an alpha particle with kinetic energy 10 MeV. What does this tell us about the size of the nucleus?

Key ideas

- In alpha particle scattering experiments, particles that turn back on themselves must have travelled very close to the nuclei of the target material.

- The distance of closest approach of these particles provides an upper estimate for the size of the nuclei.

- The electronvolt is a unit of energy used in atomic and nuclear physics. One electronvolt (eV) is the energy gained by an electron when it is accelerated through a potential difference of one volt.

1.3   The right wavelength

'Just because we model one thing on another doesn't mean they always behave the same way. We can sometimes imagine that particles in a gas are like snooker balls – just so long as we remember that they aren't exactly the same! We can imagine that electrons are like hard little pellets when they act like they are.'

Waves passing an obstacle are **diffracted**: they spread out into the space behind the obstacle (see *Physics Core* book, p. 116). If the obstacle is about the same size as the wavelength of the waves, the effect is very strong. The waves cross each other's paths as they spread out, reinforcing each other along some lines and cancelling each other along other lines. This **interference** produces a distinctive pattern (Fig. 5). The pattern is related to the size of the barrier and the wavelength of the waves.

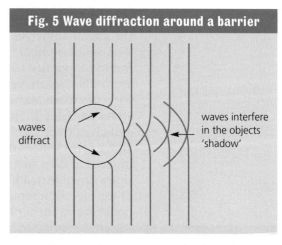

Fig. 5 Wave diffraction around a barrier

waves diffract

waves interfere in the objects 'shadow'

Investigating nuclei by studying wave diffraction needs waves that have small enough wavelengths. Electromagnetic waves are unsuitable; even the wavelength of very high energy gamma rays are just too big. The solution is to use high speed electrons. This idea is part of another 20th century revolution in physics: particles can sometimes act like waves.

Waves and particles

Electrons diffract. This might seem surprising, if you are used to thinking of electrons as particles. Electrons behave like particles in many situations, but they can also behave like waves. We need to use a wave model to explain some aspects of their behaviour, and a particle model to explain others. This double nature is referred to as **wave–particle duality** (see Chapter 8, and *Physics Core* book, p. 160).

The wavelength of an electron depends upon its momentum. Wavelength can be calculated using the **de Broglie relationship**:

$$\lambda = \frac{h}{p}$$

where λ is the wavelength of the electron, p is its momentum and h is a constant called Planck's constant (= 6.6×10^{-34} J s). The de Broglie relationship tells us that the momentum (and therefore the speed) of an electron and its wavelength are inversely related: as one increases, the other decreases.

Electrons with energies of about 1000 eV (1 keV) have wavelengths similar in magnitude to the distances between atoms in a solid. If they pass through a sample of material, the electrons diffract exactly like light waves passing through a diffraction grating (see *Physics Core* book, chapter 9). The angles of the emerging beams tell us about the separation of nuclei in the material (Fig. 6).

Fig. 6 Electrons diffracting from a sample of material

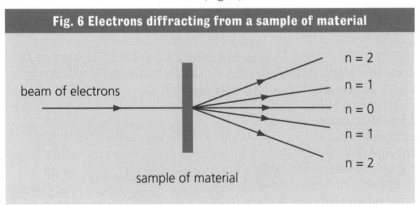

beam of electrons

sample of material

n = 2
n = 1
n = 0
n = 1
n = 2

If the energy of the electrons increases, the wavelength decreases. When the wavelength is about as small as the nuclei, the pattern of interference tells us about the nuclei themselves rather than the spacing between them (Fig. 7). The first minimum of intensity, at an angle θ, in a diffraction pattern produced by a spherical obstacle is related to the radius of the obstacle, R:

$$R = \frac{0.61\lambda}{\sin\theta}$$

Fig. 7 Electron diffraction pattern of oxygen nuclei

The diffraction of electrons provides a measurement of nuclear size. This diffraction pattern came from a beam with an energy of 125 GeV.

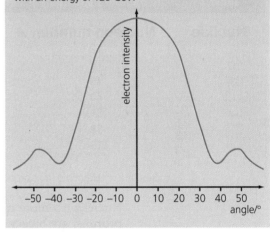

electron intensity

−50 −40 −30 −20 −10 0 10 20 30 40 50
angle/°

Studies of electron diffraction give a much more accurate estimate of nuclear radii than the 'upper estimates' obtained with alpha particle scattering. Now that we have established the scale of the nuclear model of the atom, it's time to consider the nucleus itself. How does the nucleus behave? How have scientists modelled the nucleus?

 2   Use Fig. 7 to calculate the radius of an oxygen nucleus.

Key ideas

- Electrons behave like particles in some situations and like waves in others.

- When a beam of high-energy electrons interacts with nuclei in a target material, diffraction patterns are produced.

- The detail of the diffraction patterns of very high-energy electrons can give us an estimate of the radius of nuclei. This estimate is more accurate than the upper estimate obtained from the distance of closest approach of scattered alpha particles.

1.4 Nuclear radius and nucleon number

'Measurement of nuclear sizes using electron diffraction shows that nuclei with more particles in them are bigger than nuclei with fewer particles. That might sound obvious, but nothing is obvious in the microworld of nuclei.'

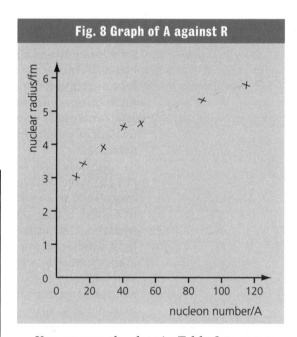

Fig. 8 Graph of A against R

Table 2 Nucleon numbers and nuclear radii for some elements

Nuclide	Nucleon number, A	Radius, R/fm
$^{12}_{6}C$	12	3.04
$^{16}_{8}O$	16	3.41
$^{28}_{14}Si$	28	3.92
$^{40}_{20}Ca$	40	4.54
$^{51}_{23}V$	51	4.63
$^{68}_{38}Sr$	88	5.34
$^{115}_{49}In$	115	5.80

1 fm = 10^{-15} m

Results from electron diffraction experiments.

Nuclei with more **nucleons** (neutrons and protons) are bigger (Table 2). This is what we might have expected. However, the pattern does not seem to be that simple: the graph of nucleon number (A) against radius (R) is not a straight line (Fig. 8).

The simplest kind of graph to interpret is a straight line through the origin. In a straight line graph, the two quantities plotted are proportional to each other and the gradient of the graph can be used to find the constant of proportionality. In other words, if a graph of y against x is a straight line through the origin with gradient k then:

$$y = kx$$

You *can* use the data in Table 2 to create a graph that approximates to a straight line, but only if you plot R^3 (instead of R) against A. The fact that this line is straight tells tells you that:

$$R^3 = kA$$

where k is the gradient of the graph.

 3 **Use Table 2 to plot a graph of R^3 against A. Draw a line of best fit (by eye) through the points and measure the gradient. What is the value of k in the relationship $R^3 = kA$?**

As R^3 is proportional to the number of nucleons, then the nuclear volume ($\frac{4}{3}\pi R^3$ if it is spherical) is also proportional to the number of nucleons. We can interpret this to mean that each nucleon contributes a certain fixed volume to the total nuclear volume.

Adding a nucleon to a nucleus therefore increases its volume by the volume of one nucleon, just as adding one more bean to the pile of beans on your toast increases the total volume of the pile (ignoring the gaps between the beans) by the volume of one bean! It sounds obvious, but it is only by knowing the relationship between nuclear volume and nucleon number that we know nucleons behave in this way, and do not merge into one another. We can go on to say that nuclei, just like different-sized piles of beans, all have approximately the same density. It comes as some relief that we can model something as incomprehensible as a tiny nucleus less than 10^{-14} m across on something as ordinary as a pile of beans!

We can find out more about the constant k: when A is 1, R must represent the radius of a single nucleon, r_0. From this we can deduce that:

$$r_0{}^3 = k$$

We can put this value for k back into our original equation:

$$R^3 = r_0{}^3 A$$

$$so, R = r_0 A^{\frac{1}{3}}$$

Key ideas

- The volume of a nucleus is proportional to the number of nucleons within it, and

  $R = r_0 A^{1/3}$.

- Nucleons do not merge into each other in the nucleus; instead, nucleons congregate.

- All nuclei have *approximately* the same density.

1.5 Nuclear density

The density of an object is its mass divided by its volume. For a nucleus, its mass is the total mass of its nucleons, Am_0, (where m_0 is the mass of a nucleon). So the density, ρ, of any nucleus is:

$$\rho = \frac{Am_0}{\frac{4}{3}\pi R^3}$$

but $R^3 = r_0 A$

so $\rho = \dfrac{Am_0}{\frac{4}{3}\pi r_0{}^3 A}$

$$= \frac{3m_0}{4\pi r_0{}^3}$$

This last expression contains only constants; it does not depend on the number of nucleons, A. This confirms that all nuclei have very nearly the same

density. Notice that we have assumed neutrons and protons to have an identical and fixed mass, m_0. Their masses are not in fact quite identical – nor are they constant, as you will find out in later chapters. However, the assumption is a fair one for the purposes of these calculations.

The mass of a nucleus is often expressed in terms of **atomic mass units**, u. One atomic mass unit is defined as one twelfth of the mass of an atom of carbon-12 ($u = 1.661 \times 10^{-27}$ kg). One atomic mass unit is *approximately* the mass of one nucleon, so the mass of a gold-197 nucleus is approximately $197u$.

We now have enough information to work out the approximate density of a gold nucleus. From your graph (question 3) you should be able to calculate that the radius of a gold-197 nucleus is about 6.5×10^{-15} m).

The approximate density of a nucleus of gold-197 is given by:

$$\text{density} = \frac{\text{mass}}{\text{volume}}$$
$$= \frac{197.0 \times 1.661 \times 10^{-27}}{\frac{4}{3} \times \left(6.5 \times 10^{-15}\right)^3}$$
$$= 1.4 \times 10^{18} \ \text{kg m}^{-3}$$

This is approximately the density of any nucleus.

4 Use a data book to find out the atomic radius and relative atomic mass of gold.
a Calculate the volume of one gold atom.
b Calculate the mass of one gold atom.
c Using your answers to parts a and b, calculate the density of one gold atom.
d Compare your answer for part c with the density of a nucleus. Give reasons for the large difference between the density of a gold atom and that of a nucleus.

5 a Estimate the volume of your body that is made up of nuclei.
b What does the rest of the volume of your body contain?

Key ideas

• Nuclei have a very high density: approximately 10^{15} times the density of water.

1.6 Forces between nucleons

We see the gravitational force at work all of the time, and we can feel the effects of electrical forces. The gravitational force is dominant where large bodies such as stars, planets and people are interacting.

Electrostatic forces dominate behaviour on an atomic scale.

The force that determines the behaviour of nucleons inside nuclei is neither gravitational nor electrical. Gravitational

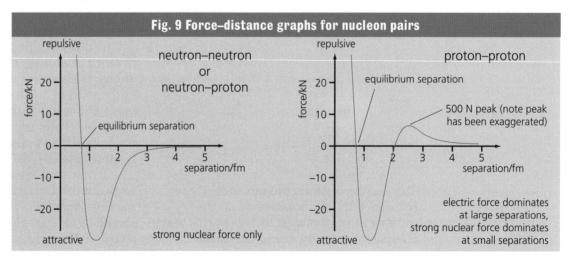

Fig. 9 Force–distance graphs for nucleon pairs

force between bodies with mass as small as that of nucleons is very weak. Neutrons are not affected by electrostatic forces at all, and the electrostatic force between protons is highly repulsive, so without the presence of another force, nuclei would blast apart. The fact that nucleons come together at all tells us that there must be some other force at work inside a nucleus which we do not experience in the human-sized world.

We call this force the **strong nuclear force** or the **strong interaction**. It must be strong enough to overcome the electrostatic repulsion between closely-packed protons.

We have seen that nucleons cluster together – they do not merge into one point. Therefore, at some point when nucleons are very close together, they must stop attracting each other and start to repel. This is similar to how particles in solids and liquids attract each other over a range of distances, but repel one another when they are very close. Fig. 9 shows how the force between nucleons varies with their separation.

6 There are no stable nuclei with more than about 200 nucleons. What does this suggest about the range over which the strong nuclear force can act?

7 At which two distances apart is the force between two neutrons equal to zero?

The concept of potential energy is very useful for predicting the behaviour of particles. The most stable state of any

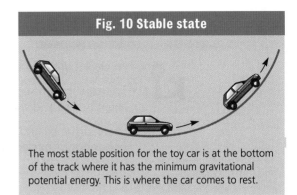

Fig. 10 Stable state

The most stable position for the toy car is at the bottom of the track where it has the minimum gravitational potential energy. This is where the car comes to rest.

system is the one in which its bodies have the least possible potential energy (Fig. 10).

If we know how much potential energy two bodies have at different distances apart, we can predict the distance apart at which they will come to rest. A pair of nucleons has minimum potential energy when they are a certain distance apart. The two nucleons will always tend to settle this far apart: the distance is called their **equilibrium separation** (Fig. 11).

8 a From the illustrations, determine the equilibrium separation of two neutrons.

  b Draw two dots to represent neutrons that are the equilibrium separation distance apart. Below the dots, using the same scale for distance, sketch force–distance and potential energy–distance graphs.

9 Two protons come close enough together for the system to have positive potential energy. Predict what will happen next.

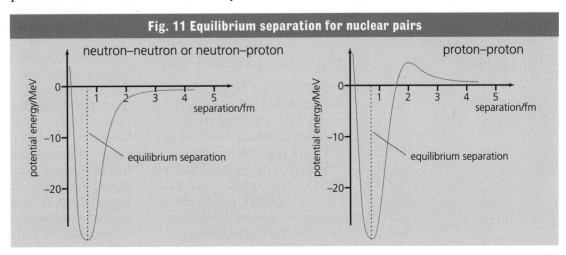

Fig. 11 Equilibrium separation for nuclear pairs

Key ideas

- Nucleons are held together in the nucleus by the strong nuclear force.

- The equilibrium separation of two particles is the distance at which the net force between them is zero and the potential energy is at a minimum.

- Force–distance and potential energy–distance graphs provide useful representations of the behaviour of nucleons.

1.7 A new model

'Nuclei are a lot smaller than drops of liquid. But there are some comparisons that help us to picture what goes on in nuclei. Liquid drops make good model nuclei.

You have to be able to switch between different models of the same thing. Atoms are like hard spheres, fuzzy clouds or energy levels – depending on exactly what you are trying to get your head around.'

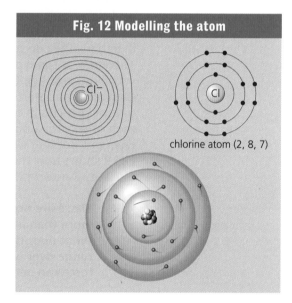

Fig. 12 Modelling the atom

chlorine atom (2, 8, 7)

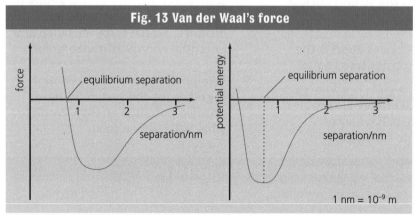

Fig. 13 Van der Waal's force

1 nm = 10⁻⁹ m

The behaviour of liquids is determined by the intermolecular **van der Waal's** force. The shapes of the force–distance curve and the potential energy–distance curve for the intermolecular force (Fig. 13) are very similar to those for the strong nuclear force (Fig. 9 and Fig. 11). The biggest difference between the two sets of graphs is in the scale of the *x*-axis. Because of the strong similarities between the force–distance

graphs, the behaviour of the molecules in a drop of liquid is a useful model for the behaviour of the nucleons within a nucleus.

10 By what factor does the range of inter-atomic force differ from the range of inter-nucleon force?

The similarities between nucleon behaviour and the behaviour of the molecules in a drop of liquid goes beyond the shapes of the force–distance graphs. Drops of liquid have a density which is independent of their size, just like nuclei. Molecules can escape from a liquid drop by evaporation, just as nucleons can escape from a nucleus during some kinds of radioactive emission. Liquid drops do not grow above a certain size, and neither do nuclei. Very large drops break up into smaller drops, and so do nuclei. Like all models, the liquid drop idea has weaknesses as well as strengths. A nucleus is like a liquid drop in some ways, but not in others (Table 3).

Nuclei are way beyond the reach of human senses. It is only by using the techniques of measurement and modelling that we can ever hope to understand them.

 11 Nucleon emission from nuclei is rare. Evaporation of molecules from a liquid drop is not. What aspect of the water drop model of the nucleus departs from a real water drop to explain this difference?

Table 3 Strengths and weaknesses of liquid drop model		
Property	**Nucleus**	**Liquid drop**
force between particles	attraction between nucleons close to one another, but repulsion at very close range	attraction between molecules close to one another, but repulsion at very close range
density	constant internal density	constant internal density
dynamic	nucleus can oscillate and split into two parts; free nucleons are emitted only by very unstable nuclei	drop can oscillate and split into two or more parts; individual molecules may escape (evaporate)
surface	show surface tension effects	show surface tension effects

Key ideas

- The strong nuclear force is similar in many ways to the van der Waal's intermolecular force.

- A liquid drop provides a useful model for the behaviour of a nucleus. Observing the behaviour of liquid molecules can lead to a better understand of the behaviour of nucleons.

Accelerating costs

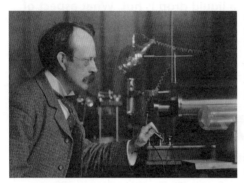

J. J. Thomson.

At the end of the nineteenth century, Joseph Thomson worked with cathode-ray tubes at Cambridge University. His observations led to the discovery of electrons. Without the discovery of the electron and its behaviour, electronics, telecommunications and most of modern chemistry would not exist at all.

In October 1993, plans for the biggest ever device for studying the structure of matter – the superconducting supercollider (SSC) – were scrapped. The SSC was an eleven billion dollar project (about seven billion pounds sterling), and would have

been an 83 kilometre-long oval tunnel buried deep beneath the ground in Waxahachie, Texas. Particle physicists wanted to use the collider to 'smash' atoms.

US politicians voted to scrap the planned SSC by 282 votes to 143 after two billion dollars had been spent. Would the SSC have revolutionised both ideas and technologies in the same way as the cathode-ray tube?

Inside the scrapped SSC.

The world of electronic media.

2.1 Learning objectives

After working through this chapter, you should be able to:

- **explain** the principles of the cyclotron proton accelerator and the Van de Graaff accelerator;
- **describe** the behaviour of charged particles in electric and magnetic fields;
- **explain** how a linear accelerator, a synchrotron and a cyclotron work;
- **describe** the use of ionisation chambers, spark counters and Geiger–Müller tubes.

Simple accelerators

As particles gain energy, they behave more like the particles that were around during the first fractions of a second of the Big Bang (in theory, the beginning of the Universe over 15 billion years ago). High-energy accelerators create events that are unnatural to today's relatively cold world.

Particle physicists aim to probe deeper and deeper into the structure of matter, beyond the nucleus, deep inside protons and neutrons. Researchers study the ways in which particles interact with each other, and attempt to identify patterns. To look at smaller and smaller particles requires the use of bigger and bigger accelerators (Fig. 1).

When particles collide, new particles can be formed. The total mass of the new particles can be greater than that of the original particles. The kinetic energy of the original particles can be converted into mass according to the mass–energy formula: $E = mc^2$. Only very fast particles have enough energy for the physicists to study the creation of new particles. Accelerators that provide very fast particles are more expensive.

The Van de Graaff generator

A Van de Graaff generator is an old but relatively cheap way of accelerating particles. The generator accumulates electric charge on a metal dome (Fig. 2). This creates an electric field in the space around the dome. If the field

Fig. 1 History of particle accelerators

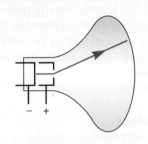

name cathode ray tube	van de Graaff generator	electron microscope
particles electrons	protons/small ions	electrons
particle energy 1 keV (1×10^3 V)	10 MeV (10×10^6 V)	25 keV (25×10^3 V)
discoveries mass and charge of electron	structure of nuclei	structure of crystals, viruses and cells

name cyclotron	linear accelerator	synchrotron
particles protons/small ions	electrons/positrons/protons	protons
particle energy 25 MeV (25×10^6 V)	50 GeV (50×10^9 V)	1 TeV (1×10^{12} V)
discoveries structure of nuclei and transmutation of elements	evidence for quarks, tau lepton	bottom quark, exchange particles

Fig. 2 Van de Graaff accelerator

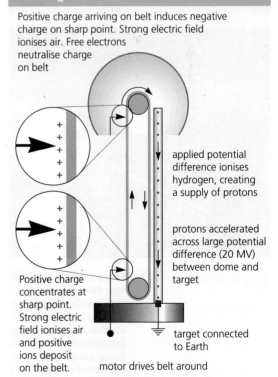

Positive charge arriving on belt induces negative charge on sharp point. Strong electric field ionises air. Free electrons neutralise charge on belt

applied potential difference ionises hydrogen, creating a supply of protons

protons accelerated across large potential difference (20 MV) between dome and target

Positive charge concentrates at sharp point. Strong electric field ionises air and positive ions deposit on the belt.

target connected to Earth

motor drives belt around

is strong enough to ionise the air, it can produce dramatic sparks. Any charged particle (a speck of dust or a proton for example) within the electric field around the dome experiences a force, and will accelerate. The generator is therefore a simple particle accelerator. Large modern particle accelerators work on the same principle – accelerating charges through a potential difference.

If the accelerated particles gain enough energy they can be absorbed by the nuclei of the target material's atoms. This process is commonly used to create radioactive isotopes for medical, industrial and research purposes.

The kinetic energy gained by a proton moving between the dome and earth is given by:

energy gained = electrical charge × potential difference

If the potential difference between the dome and earth is 5×10^6 V,

energy gained $= 1.6 \times 10^{-19}$ C $\times 5 \times 10^6$ V

$= 8 \times 10^{-13}$ J

You can see that the joule is a large unit for measuring the energy of an individual particle. In particle physics, the

Table 1 Particle masses		
Particle	**symbol**	**mass (in MeV)**
proton	p	938.3
antiproton	$\bar{p}$	938.3
neutron	n	939.6
antineutron	$\bar{n}$	939.6
electron	e⁻	0.51
antielectron	e⁺	0.51
neutrino	v	0(?)
antineutrino	$\bar{v}$	0(?)
pion	π^+	139.6
	π^-	139.6
	π^0	135.0
kaon	k⁺	493.7
	k⁻	493.7
	k⁰	497.7

electronvolt is often used instead of the joule:

One electronvolt, eV, is defined as the kinetic energy transferred to a particle with the same amount of charge as an electron when it is accelerated through a potential difference of one volt. One electronvolt is equal to 1.6×10^{-19} J.

In the above case, the proton gains 5×10^6 eV (or 5 MeV) of kinetic energy, as it moves across a potential difference of 5×10^6 V.

Mass and energy are interconvertible ($E = mc^2$), so particle mass is often given in units of energy (Table 1), or MeV/c^2.

1 Calculate the kinetic energy gained by a proton when it accelerates through a vacuum with a potential difference of 10 MV across it. State your answer in joules and electronvolts.

Linear accelerators

A simple **linear accelerator** consists of a line of tubes, positioned end-to-end that charged particles can travel along (Fig. 3).

At the Stanford Linear Accelerator, near San Francisco, USA, electrons 'ride' on electromagnetic waves that effectively create electric fields, accelerating them almost continuously for 3 km. The Stanford Linear Accelerator (SLAC) can accelerate electrons up to energies of 50 GeV.

Fig. 3 Linear accelerator

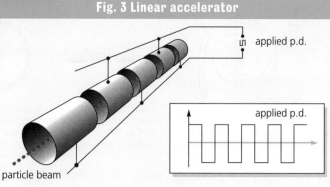

applied p.d.

applied p.d.

particle beam

An alternating voltage is applied to the tubes so that as they move through the gap between the two tubes, the particles are repelled by the tube behind them and attracted to the tube in front. Keeping the alternating voltage synchronised with the movement of the particles from tube to tube is crucial. To make up for the fact that the particles are going faster and faster as they move along the tunnel, it is necessary to either increase the frequency of the alternating voltage or use sections of increasing length. If the sections are short at the start and longer at the end, the particles can be in each section for the same amount of time.

Key ideas

- Particle physicists use fast (high-energy) particles, to study particle interactions that do not normally occur.
- Particles accelerated to high speed can be used to change the structure of nuclei within the atoms of a target material.

2.3 Circular accelerators

'Here at Loma Linda University Medical Center we treat over 100 cancer patients a day using a specially designed synchrotron. We have recently bought some 'desktop' cyclotrons to keep us supplied with the radioisotopes that are so valuable to other radiotherapy work such as gamma-imaging.'

The length of linear accelerators can put a practicable limit on their use. This problem can be solved by rolling up a linear accelerator into a spiral. You should recall (see *Physics Core* book) that moving charged particles can be made to move in a circle by applying a magnetic field.

The first circular accelerators, called **cyclotrons**, used a simple magnetic field to confine the accelerating particles. Like the Van de Graaff generator, cyclotrons use an electric field to accelerate the particles (usually protons). The electric field is created

The world's first cyclotron, built in 1930 by E. O. Lawrence. It could accelerate protons to energies of 8 MeV. More recent cyclotrons are capable of accelerating protons up to 100 MeV. Lawrence often kept his cyclotron running all night to produce radioisotopes for nearby California hospitals.

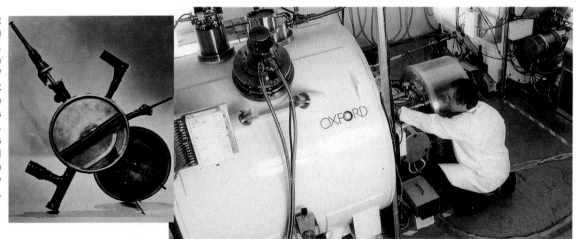

This 'desktop' cyclotron is sold by the british company Oxford Instruments. It is an essential source of isotopes for PET scans, but it only consumes 1 kW of power because of its innovative superconducting magnet technology.

19

Fig. 4 A simple cyclotron

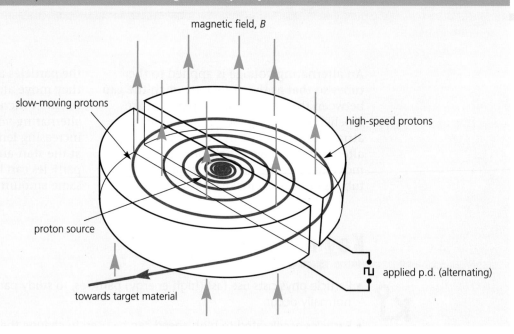

magnetic field, B

slow-moving protons

high-speed protons

proton source

applied p.d. (alternating)

towards target material

by applying a voltage between the two D shaped pieces (Fig. 4). At any one moment, one D has a positive potential (which repels the positively charged protons), while the other D has negative potential (which attracts protons). By alternating the applied voltage to each D, protons are accelerated by being attracted to alternate Ds. In one cycle of the alternating voltage, all the protons in the cyclotron complete one circular 'lap' of the cyclotron.

While the Van de Graaff accelerator depends upon a single, large voltage to accelerate protons, the cyclotron uses a smaller voltage many times over. A proton passes from one D to the other many times as it spirals out from the centre of the cyclotron. Each time a proton moves from one D to the other, it receives another 'kick' forwards from the potential difference between the Ds.

The magnetic field pushes any moving charged particles with a force at right angles to the particle's motion. This provides the centripetal force necessary for the circular motion. If the speed of the protons is v, their mass m, their charge Q, the radius of their path r, and the magnetic field strength B, we can write:

magnetic force = centripetal force

$$BQv = \frac{mv^2}{r}$$

$$r = \frac{mv}{BQ}$$

We would expect the mass (m) and the charge (Q) of the proton to remain constant. If the magnetic field (B) is constant, you can see that the radius of a protons' circular motion is proportional to that protons velocity ($r \propto v$). As the protons move from D to D, their speed increases. This means that the protons trace out larger and larger circles in a spiral motion.

As the particles approach the speed of light, their mass *does* begin to increase significantly (see Chapter 12). This tends to increase both the radius of the particles' path and the time to complete a 'lap' of the cyclotron. The proton's circular paths and the alternating voltage lose their synchronisation. Further acceleration is hopeless. This limits the amount of energy that a cyclotron can transfer to protons.

Synchrotrons

A synchrotron, such as the Large Electron–Positron Collider at CERN, is a more sophisticated circular accelerator than the cyclotron. The magnetic field is adjusted in strength in a much more complex way to allow for the synchronisation problems that a cyclotron faces with very fast 'relativistic' particles.

To keep the magnetic field strength down to manageable levels, the radius of the particles' paths is much larger than in a cyclotron. This means that the accelerator is in the form of a large loop (not a disc like the cyclotron) and the radius of the particles' path must be constant at all times (Fig. 5).

The Large Electron–Positron (LEP) accelerator at CERN, the European Organisation for Nuclear Research, in Geneva, accelerates electrons and positrons (positively charged electrons) in opposite directions around adjacent pipes. The LEP can force particles together at energies of 100 GeV.

Synchrotrons are heavily dependent on magnet technology. This large and costly superconducting magnet is being readied for use in CERNs Large Hadron Collider. Much modern superconductivity technology is owed to the effort of synchrotron engineers in the past.

Fig. 5 A synchrotron

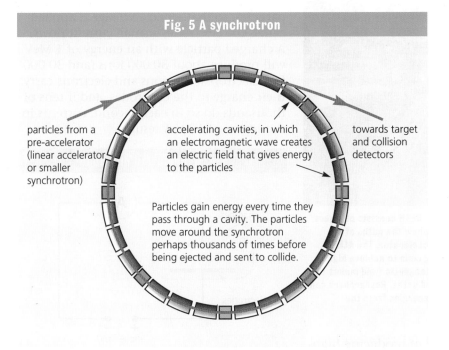

particles from a pre-accelerator (linear accelerator or smaller synchrotron)

accelerating cavities, in which an electromagnetic wave creates an electric field that gives energy to the particles

towards target and collision detectors

Particles gain energy every time they pass through a cavity. The particles move around the synchrotron perhaps thousands of times before being ejected and sent to collide.

For any magnetic field strength B, the radius of the path depends on the velocity of the particles (from $r = mv/BQ$). If v increases, the particles spiral out; if v decreases, the particles spiral in. In both cases the particles leave the accelerating track. This restricts the synchrotron to accelerating bursts of particles that are all at the same speed.

2 a Calculate the energy gained by a proton in a cyclotron when it moves from one D to the other, if the potential difference between the Ds is 8 kV. State your answers in joules and electronvolts.

b Calculate the speed of a proton that has made 1000 such transfers.

c Calculate the radius of the path for the proton in part b, if the magnetic field strength is 0.8 T.

d Approximately how long will it take the proton to complete one semi-circular journey through each D?

e What frequency of the alternating voltage would synchronise with the proton's path to accelerate it?

3 Sketch a graph that shows the cycle in applied p.d. against time for the Ds in a cyclotron. Describe the path taken by a proton, explaining what is happening to the proton at each point in the cycle.

4 List the advantages of a fixed radius particle path in a synchrotron, compared with the spiralling path in a cyclotron.

5 Give two reasons why it is necessary to increase magnetic field strength in a synchrotron as the particles accelerate.

Key ideas

- Charged particles can be accelerated to very high energies in linear accelerators and synchrotrons.

- In a cyclotron, an electric field accelerates protons, while a magnetic field makes the protons spiral around inside semi-circular Ds.

- Cyclotrons cannot accelerate particles to speeds very close to the speed of light.

- Higher particle speeds can be achieved in a synchrotron than in a cyclotron.

- Synchrotrons can only accelerate particles that are all at the same speed.

2.4 Detecting results

The ALEPH particle detector at CERN consists of layers of 'solid state' detectors that show the paths of the particles emerging from the accelerator. The ALEPH detector uses superconducting coils to achieve high magnetic field strengths. The magnetic field makes the charged particles follow curved paths. Researchers can calculate particle speeds and energies from the curvature of the paths.

Accelerators are capable of producing high-speed particles, but particle physicists need detection equipment to observe the interactions that take place. At the frontiers of particle physics, the detectors are, like accelerators, huge and extremely expensive. Detectors of sub-atomic particles cannot detect the actual particles. Instead they detect the ionisation that the particles produce in materials they pass through.

Ionisation chamber

An ionisation chamber is a simple detector (Fig. 6). Any ionised particles passing between the two electrodes will collide with atoms of the gas in the chamber and ionise them. This produces charged particles, so that when a voltage is applied across the electrodes a small current flows. A charged particle with an energy of 1 MeV will produce about 30 000 ions (and 30 000 free electrons). The ions and electrons carry their charge to the electrodes, and if tens of thousands do so in each second, currents in the region of 10^{-12} A result.

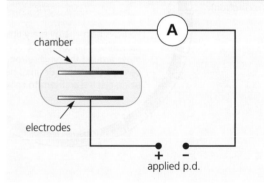

Fig. 6 Ionisation chamber

The size of the applied voltage is crucial (Fig. 7). If the voltage is too low, many of the ions and free electrons will recombine before they reach the electrodes. The resulting current is too small to detect. If the voltage is too high, it can attract electrons from the gas atoms without the need for ionising particles.

Fig. 7 Effect of applied p.d. for simple particle detector

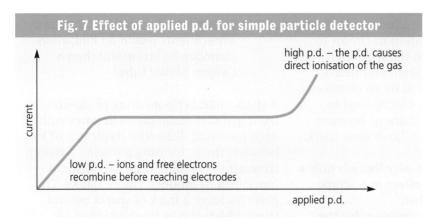

high p.d. – the p.d. causes direct ionisation of the gas

current

low p.d. – ions and free electrons recombine before reaching electrodes

applied p.d.

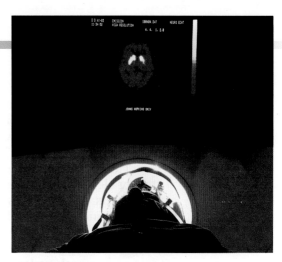

This **PET (Positron Emmission Tomography) scanner** uses crystals originally developed for semiconductor particle-detectors.

Semiconductor particle detector

A **semiconductor** (solid state) particle detector is similar in many ways to an ionisation chamber, but it has a solid rather than a gas between its electrodes. The advantage of semiconductor detectors is that in the denser solid, particles collide with atoms much more often, so that more ions and electrons are produced. This makes it easier to detect ionising particles. Ionisation of atoms produces not only free electrons, but also 'holes' in the crystal structure left by the freed electrons. The ions in a solid are not free to move, but the electrons and 'holes' can travel towards the electrodes.

Geiger–Müller tube

A Geiger–Müller tube (Fig. 8) is another type of ionisation chamber. The metal tube itself acts as one electrode, and the central rod acts as the other. Incoming particles ionise the gas molecules inside just as in an

ionisation chamber. The important difference in the Geiger–Müller tube is that the applied voltage and the gas pressure are set so that a single ionisation event produces the strongest possible 'avalanche' of ionisation. The applied voltage accelerates the ions and free electrons so that they collide with, and ionise, other atoms, which in turn collide with, and ionise, further atoms. The **avalanche effect** means that an event caused by a single ionising particle will produce a detectable current in the Geiger–Müller tube.

Spark counter

A spark counter is another detector that uses the avalanche effect. It consists of a fine metal wire fixed close to a metal plate or grid (Fig. 9). There is a high voltage (1000 V or more) between the wire and the plate. A particle passing between these causes one or more initial ionisation events

Fig. 8 The Geiger–Muller tube

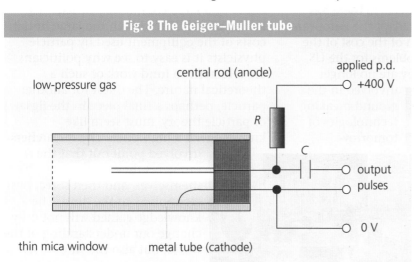

low-pressure gas

central rod (anode)

applied p.d.
+400 V

R

C

output
pulses

0 V

thin mica window   metal tube (cathode)

Fig. 9 Simple spark counter

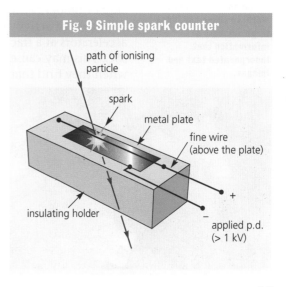

path of ionising particle

spark

metal plate

fine wire (above the plate)

insulating holder

+

–

applied p.d. (> 1 kV)

in the air. The avalanche effect that follows can cause enough ionisation in the air to produce a spark between the wire and plate. The spark can be seen, and heard. The sparks can be counted by an observer, or electronic equipment can be used to detect the short burst of current between the wire and plate, that follows each spark.

6 a Suggest a reason why there is only a weak avalanche effect in a simple ionisation chamber.

b Why is this not a problem for the detection of ionising radiation?

c For what sort of observations and experiments would an ionisation chamber be less useful than a Geiger–Müller tube?

A spark chamber is an array of closely-fixed, parallel metal plates or wires with a high potential difference (typically 10 kV) between them. Ionising particles, passing through the chamber, create sufficient ionisation to produce visible sparks. The particles leave a track of sparks behind them which can be photographed to provide a permanent record.

Key ideas

- All particle detectors depend on the ionising effects of particles.

2.5 Pushing to the limit

Scientists designing high-energy experiments are reaching the limit of energy and funding. Some scientists have even suggested accelerators in orbit around the Earth, which would take advantage of the natural vacuum. More practically, scientists are collaborating at an international level, and pooling their collective funds. In the wake of the American Superconducting Super Collider being cancelled, there has been a lot of activity to adapt the European accelerators at a fraction of the cost of the SSC. This may cause problems for the US when they find that they are no longer involved in the ground-breaking technologies of tomorrow.

The World-Wide Web was devised at CERN as a way for scientists across the world to share and index large amounts of information that incorporated text and images.

Smaller and more powerful computer chips are being manufactured using synchrotron radiation technology.

Particle physics involves a mammoth effort by a large community of scientists and engineers. Faced with the large initial costs of the equipment used by particle physicists it is easy to see why politicians are reluctant to fund work of such a theoretical nature. The quest for another particle, perhaps a final piece in the jigsaw of particle theory, must seem like knowledge at a high price. The researchers involved point out that the problems they set for themselves, and then solve, push technology to the limit. The knowledge gained will not only change our understanding of the world, but also the way we live.

Strangeness and charm in California

California has been the source of dreams for the twentieth century: blockbuster special-effects movies from Hollywood show imaginary worlds and impossible events; San Francisco was the starting place for hippies and the hell's angels that still roam the city's freeways.

California has also been the source of other dream-like ideas, which were similarly outrageous and just plain weird, in the field of physics.

California has been a powerful centre of cultural influence – from popular culture to the not-so-easy culture of exploration of the physical world. Is it a coincidence that so much should happen in the same place at the same time? Probably not. California, for most of the twentieth century, was the home of the new. It attracted new people with new dreams and ideas, concentrated them together, and the creativity flowed.

This is not 1960s' psychedelia from California, but a photograph of the tracks left by ionising, charged particles in a bubble chamber.

25

3.1 Learning objectives

After working through this chapter, you should be able to:

- **explain** how cloud chambers and bubble chambers produce visible particle tracks;

- **understand** the relationship between particles and antiparticles;

- **understand** the exchange particle model for the mechanism of forces between particles;

- **understand** how interactions between different types of sub-atomic particle provide clues to their structure;

- **use** baryon number, lepton number, charge number, and strangeness conservation rules to identify possible and impossible particle interactions;

- **describe** the characteristics of leptons and hadrons;

- **describe** the difference between baryons and mesons in terms of quarks;

- **describe** the characteristics of 'weak' interactions between particles.

3.2 Discovering antimatter

'Ye cannae change the laws of physics.' The Star Trek dilithium crystals 'regulate the matter–antimatter reaction' that powers the ship's engines.

In 1932, a Californian called Carl Anderson was studying the behaviour of **beta particles** (high-energy electrons) in a strong magnetic field. He was able to observe the paths of beta particles using a **cloud chamber** (Fig. 1).

Anderson, like other physicists, knew that the beta particles were electrons, and therefore negatively charged. The magnetic field deflected these electrons in the direction he expected. However, he also observed another similar track being deflected in the *opposite* direction.

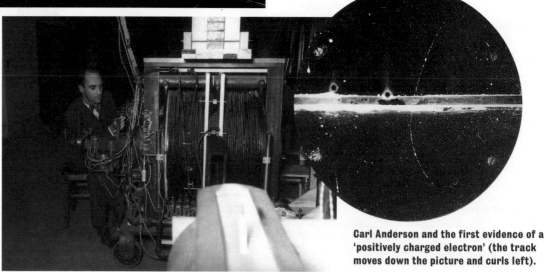

Carl Anderson and the first evidence of a 'positively charged electron' (the track moves down the picture and curls left).

Fig. 1 A simple cloud chamber

A cloud chamber contains a gas, often air, and a supersaturated vapour. Ionising particles such as beta particles ionise the air as they pass through the chamber, and the ions produced act as sites for the vapour to condense around. The liquid droplets that form along the trails of ionised air are just big enough to see and photograph.

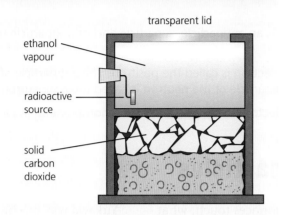

transparent lid

ethanol vapour

radioactive source

solid carbon dioxide

Anderson wrote that there seemed to be:

'a particle carrying a positive charge but having a mass of the same order of magnitude as that normally possessed by a free negative electron.'

Anderson proposed that a particle with the same mass as an electron, but with an opposite charge, produced the second track. He named the new particle a **positron**.

Fig. 2 Bubble chamber

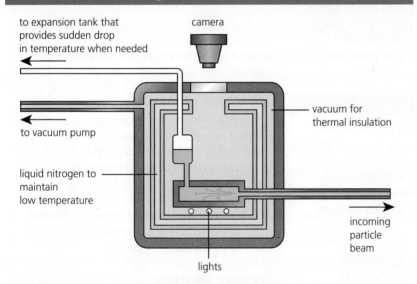

to expansion tank that provides sudden drop in temperature when needed

camera

to vacuum pump

liquid nitrogen to maintain low temperature

lights

vacuum for thermal insulation

incoming particle beam

A bubble chamber is similar to a cloud chamber, but instead of containing a supersaturated vapour, it contains a liquid. The liquid (usually hydrogen or propane) is 'super-heated' – kept from boiling by a high pressure.

A momentary release of pressure in the chamber causes the liquid to boil at the points where ions are present, i.e in the tracks of the ionising particles, and the tracks show up as lines of tiny bubbles.

Bubble chambers show more detail than cloud chambers because particles collide more often with the atoms of the denser liquid medium.

Unknown to Anderson, a British physicist, Paul Dirac, had already predicted that for every particle, such as the electron, there could be a another particle with matching mass but opposite electric charge. Dirac had combined ideas from the mathematics of Einstein's **Special Relativity** with the outrageously new ideas of **quantum mechanics**, to come to this conclusion. Dirac called the new particles **antiparticles**. Anderson's discovery made people realise that Dirac's prediction of the existence of antimatter was more than just a crazy theory.

With the development of bubble chambers (Fig. 2) in the 1950s, **pair production** events were commonly seen. In these events, a **photon**, which is very weakly ionising and leaves no clear trail of bubbles, ceases to exist. Its energy appears as an electron and a positron, seemingly from nothing!

When an electron and a positron meet, the opposite of pair production occurs. The electron and positron annihilate each other, and the energy associated with their masses appears as the energy of a pair of photons.

1 Use the Data section to draw a table showing the masses and charges of electrons, protons, neutrons and their antiparticles.

2a The masses of the electron and the positron are both 9×10^{-31} kg. Use $E = mc^2$ (see Chapter 12) to calculate the total energy of a pair of photons produced by an electron–positron annihilation event. (The photons are identical and $c = 3.0 \times 10^8$ m s^{-1}.)

b What will be the frequency of each photon?

c Given that photon energy and frequency are related by $E = hf$, where h is Planck's constant, what is the minimum possible frequency of a single photon if its energy is to create an electron and a positron?

d If the photon has more energy than the minimum amount, what could happen to the surplus energy after the pair production?

Key ideas

- For every particle there is an antiparticle. A particle and its antiparticle have the same mass but opposite charge.

- The antiparticle of the electron is called the positron. The antiparticle of the proton is called the antiproton. The antiparticle of the neutron is called the antineutron.

- The production of an electron and a positron from photon energy is called pair production.

3.3 Exchanging particles

Hideki Yukawa.

When we say that two surfaces touch, what we mean is that they are close enough for the forces between the two surfaces to be repulsive. Even when your finger is 'in contact' with your pen, the particles of pen and particles of finger are not actually zero distance apart. The forces between the particles act over a distance, in this case a very small distance. What makes two objects attract or repel each other? What is going on in the space between objects?

The Japanese physicist Hideki Yukawa used the ideas of pair production and 'virtual particles' to suggest that forces could be caused by **exchange particles**. Yukawa used Heisenberg's Uncertainty Principle (see box), which says that energy can be 'borrowed' for the creation of particles, provided that it is soon 'paid back'.

The Uncertainty Principle

Producing pairs of particles from the energy of photons may seem odd, but it gets odder: pairs of particles can be created from no energy at all! According to a law of physics called Heisenberg's Uncertainty Principle, an amount of energy ΔE can be borrowed for up to a time Δt as long as the product of ΔE and Δt is not be bigger than a certain value, h. This value is 6.626×10^{-34} J s, and is called Planck's constant:

$$\Delta E \times \Delta t < h$$

This process of 'borrowing' allows short-lived events to occur that would otherwise need extra energy. At the very small scale, energy is creating and destroying 'virtual particles' all the time, even in a 'vacuum'. What once was imagined as literally *nothing* is now imagined as a bubbling soup of virtual particle–antiparticle pairs. Don't worry if this makes no sense right now. Heisenberg wasn't from California, but it is still a *very* odd idea, and it works.

Yukawa was specifically working on the **strong nuclear force**, which holds neutrons and protons together in nuclei. He guessed that the force could be due to exchange particles travelling near to the speed of light. As the strong force only seems to act at the scale of a nucleus, around 10^{-15} m, Yukawa calculated that the exchange particles would have to exist for:

$$v = \frac{x}{t} \text{ or } t = \frac{x}{v}$$
$$t \approx \frac{10^{-15}}{10^{8}} \approx 10^{-23} \text{ seconds}$$

Such short-lived particles could 'borrow' a relatively large amount of energy for their mass. From more detailed and precise calculations like these, Yukawa was able to predict a mass for these particles that acted as a 'carrier' for the force.

Nobody was convinced by the exchange particle model for the strong nuclear force, until Yukawa's predicted particles appeared in cloud chamber photographs. The particles (discovered in 1947) matched Yukawa's description of exchange particles and had the right mass. These exchange particles for the strong nuclear force were named pi-mesons, or **pions**.

Feynman diagrams

Richard Feynman working at the California Institute of Technology devised simple diagrams to represent particle exchange and interaction. **Feynman diagrams** show the paths of two particles and an exchange particle going between them (Fig. 3). The diagrams are like plan views of two gliding ice-skaters who throw a ball between them.

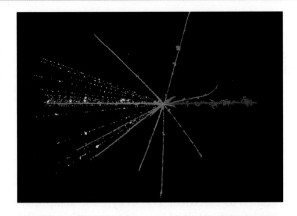

A collision with a cosmic ray produces a spray of particles, including 16 pions (shown in yellow).

Weinberg and Salam's theories predicted the masses of these exchange particles, which came to be called W and Z bosons (Fig. 4). The two physicists went so far as to say that the weak and electrical interactions were two aspects of the same thing. The world of physics was so struck by their ideas, even though their theory was unsupported by evidence, that Weinberg and Salam became Nobel Prize winners.

Fig. 3 Feynman diagrams of exchange particles

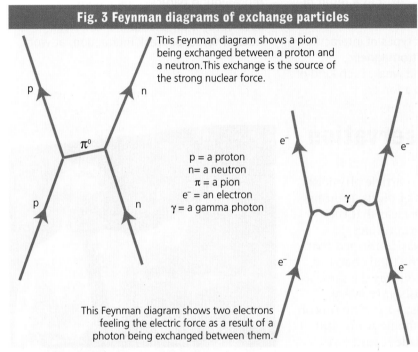

This Feynman diagram shows a pion being exchanged between a proton and a neutron.This exchange is the source of the strong nuclear force.

p = a proton
n = a neutron
π = a pion
e⁻ = an electron
γ = a gamma photon

This Feynman diagram shows two electrons feeling the electric force as a result of a photon being exchanged between them.

Abdus Salaam.

Fig. 4 Feynman diagram of beta decay

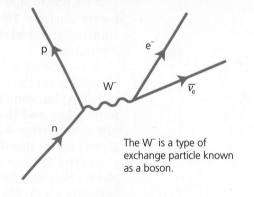

The W⁻ is a type of exchange particle known as a boson.

Richard Feynman.

At the moment of throwing the ball, and at the moment of catching the ball, the skaters experience a force. The skaters effectively repel each other, with the ball acting as an exchange particle. (The whole exchange-particle model is slightly more complicated than this to account for attractive forces.)

The exchange particle idea was quickly extended to electromagnetic forces, where it was suggested that photons were the exchange particles.

The weak interaction

Beta decay, the decay of a neutron into a proton, an electron and an antineutrino (Fig. 4), is an example of a type of particle interaction called the **weak interaction**. In the 1970s, Stephen Weinberg in California, and Abdus Salam, in London, were working on the theory that the weak interaction depends on the exchange of particles.

In 1983, evidence of the W and Z particles was found in collisions between protons and antiprotons at CERN in Switzerland. The two researchers involved also became Nobel prize winners.

Physicists would very much like to use the same kind of particle exchange model to help them think about gravitational forces. The carrier of gravity, the **graviton**, has yet to be detected.

3 Sketch a Feynman diagram for an electric interaction between two protons.

4 If Yukawa's pions only act over the 10^{-15} m range, estimate their possible maximum mass in MeV. (Use $\Delta t = 10^{-23}$ s and $\Delta E = mc^2$.)

Key ideas

- Forces between particles (such as electrical or strong nuclear forces) exist as a result of exchange of other 'particles'.

- There are four different types of interaction between particles: electromagnetic, gravitational, strong and weak. Each kind of interaction gives rise to a force.

- Feynman diagrams are a simple way of representing particle interactions.

- Beta decay is an example of the weak nuclear force, or weak interaction, at work.

3.4 Rules of conservation

In the 1950s and 1960s, particle physicists studied the interactions of pions, protons and neutrons. It became clear that the interactions followed certain rules.

Not surprisingly, it was confirmed that charge was conserved: the total charge at the end of any interaction was the same as that at the start. Physicists gave every particle a charge number, +1 for the proton and the positron, 0 for the neutron, and –1 for the electron. This made it easier to count up the total charge before and after interactions.

It became clear that the total number of particles from the neutron–proton family, called the **baryon** family, was always the same before and after an interaction. So, just as for charge numbers, particles were given **baryon numbers** which were conserved. Protons and neutrons were given a baryon number of +1, and their antiparticles –1. Electrons and neutrinos were given a baryon number of 0. Baryon number, like charge number, is conserved in all interactions.

Even with all these rules to follow, some particles were still behaving strangely. Particles called K-mesons, or **kaons**, were discovered in the decay of some neutral particles. The strange thing was that they always appeared in pairs. The kaons were never produced individually, even though

Murray Gell-Mann.

the rules of conservation of charge and baryon number did not prohibit this. Murray Gell-Mann, one of Richard Feynman's colleagues at CalTech, suggested that the interactions must follow a third rule – not the conservation of charge or baryon number, but the conservation of some other property as yet unthought of. This third property became known as **strangeness**.

When Gell-Mann gave a strangeness number of +1, 0, –1 or –2 to particles, interactions did appear to be following this third conservation rule.

Fig. 5 Conservation rules in action

The decay of a neutron: $n \rightarrow p + e^- + \bar{v}_e$

Charge number	0	1	-1	0
Baryon number	1	1	0	0
Strangeness	0	0	0	0

A proton and a pion convert into a kaon and a lambda particle $p + \pi^- \rightarrow K^0 + \Lambda^0$

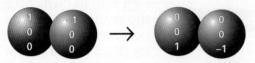

Charge number	1	-1	0	0
Baryon number	0	0	0	0
Strangeness	0	0	1	-1

Pair production: $\gamma \rightarrow e^- + e^+$

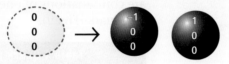

Charge number	0	-1	1
Baryon number	0	0	0
Strangeness	0	0	0

Production of an exchange particle: $p \rightarrow p + \pi^0$

Charge number	1	1	0
Baryon number	1	1	0
Strangeness	0	0	0

Acceptance of an exchange particle: $n + \pi^0 \rightarrow n$

Charge number	0	0	0
Baryon number	1	0	1
Strangeness	0	0	0

California culture.
Strangeness everywhere.

5 Draw a table to show the baryon numbers of protons, neutrons, electrons, neutrinos and their antiparticles.

6 Use the Data section to decide which of the following interactions can never occur?
- **a** $p + \pi^- \rightarrow p + \pi^+$
- **b** $K^0 \rightarrow \pi^+ + \pi^-$
- **c** $p \rightarrow \pi^+ + \pi^0$
- **d** $\gamma + p \rightarrow n + \pi^0$

Quarks and the 'Eightfold Way'

New particles and antiparticles were being discovered in bubble chambers all the time. Three types of pion were found: positive, negative and neutral; similarly for the kaons. (Then there was the muon and the neutrino and even strange 'hyperons'.)

Gell-Mann recognised that physics was faced with the same messy problem that faced chemistry in the nineteenth century.

Tell me, Sariputta, of what sort is the stream?
'The stream, lord, is just this eightfold way: right view, right thought, right speech, right action, right livelihood, right effort, right mindfullness, right concentration.'
Well said, Sariputta! The stream is just this eightfold way... Of what sort is a stream-winner, Sariputta?
'Whosoever, lord, is blessed with this eightfold way is called Streamwinner.'
Extract from the Buddhist text 'Kindred Sayings on Streamwinning' chapter I.

Instead of there being a large number of elements and reactions between them, there was a multitude of particles that needed ordering in a 'periodic table' of their own. Together with others, Gell-Mann found ways of arranging the particles according to their properties. The name he gave to the resulting patterns came from Buddhism – he called them 'the eightfold way' (Figs 6 and 7).

Fig. 6 The eightfold way for a family of baryons

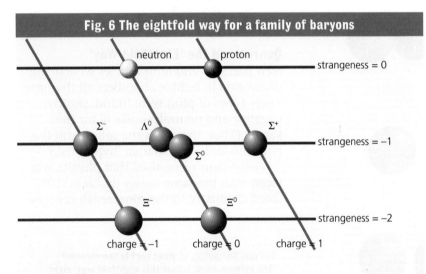

These eight baryons all have a bayon number of 1. There is a similar grid for the antiparticles (baryon number −1). The Λ^0 and Σ^0 differ only in their energy.

Fig. 7 The eightfold way for a family of mesons

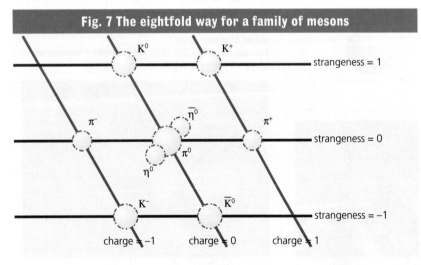

Just as the periodic table successfully predicted the existence of unknown chemical elements, the eightfold way predicted the existence of new particles. Many of these particles were found when scientists designed the right experiments to look for them.

In 1964, Gell-Mann suggested a possible reason for the patterns of the eightfold way. He suggested that the particles were made up of more fundamental particles, which he called **quarks**. Gell-Mann hypothesised that a baryon, such as a neutron or a proton was composed of three quarks, and the property of each baryon was the combination of the properties of its quarks. He proposed three kinds of quark, each with its own charge, baryon number and strangeness, and three antiquarks with exactly opposite properties. These quarks are called the **up** (u), the **down** (d) and the **strange** (s) (Table 1).

Baryons are combinations of three kinds of quark (Fig. 8). **Mesons** (pions and kaons) are combinations of one quark and one antiquark (Fig. 9).

Table 1 Quark properties			
Type	**Baryon no.**	**Charge no.**	**Strangeness**
u	1/3	2/3	0
d	1/3	−1/3	0
s	1/3	−1/3	−1
$\bar{u}$	−1/3	−2/3	0
$\bar{d}$	−1/3	1/3	0
$\bar{s}$	−1/3	1/3	+1

7 Use Table 1 to explain the total charge, baryon number and strangeness of a lambda (Λ^0) particle (see Fig. 6).

8 What is the fundamental difference between baryons and mesons?

9 Use the Data section and conservation rules to say whether the following interactions can occur. For each one, describe what does (or would) happen to quarks in the interaction.
a $\pi^+ + p \rightarrow K^+ + \Sigma^+$
b $\Lambda^0 \rightarrow \pi^+ + \pi^-$

10 Describe beta decay in terms of the change in quarks.

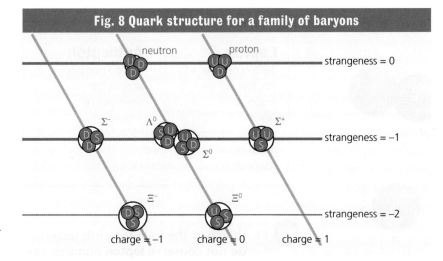

Fig. 8 Quark structure for a family of baryons

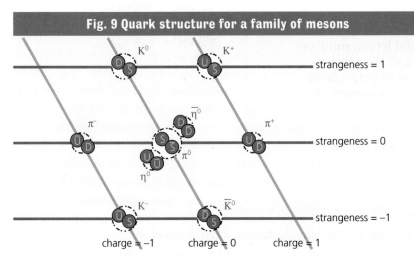

Fig. 9 Quark structure for a family of mesons

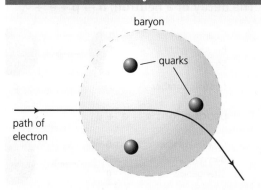

Fig. 10 Electron scattering by quarks within a baryon

Evidence for the existence of quarks. In the late 1960s, physicists at the Stanford Linear Accelerator in California beamed high energy (6 GeV) electrons into target materials. Most of the electrons passed straight through the nucleons in the materials, but some were deflected through very large angles. This can only be explained if the mass of a nucleon is not spread evenly over its whole volume, but concentrated into small points within it.

Key ideas

- Charge number, strangeness and baryon number are conserved in particle interactions.

- The baryons and the mesons together make up the hadron family of particles.

- Baryons contain three quarks. Antibaryons contain three antiquarks. Mesons contain a quark–antiquark pair.

3.5 The standard model

Protons, neutrons and pions are not *fundamental* particles. They are made of quarks. As far as we can tell, quarks are fundamental particles – they are not made up of anything simpler. Electrons, positrons and neutrinos are not made of quarks.

Electrons, positrons and neutrinos are part of another family of fundamental particles. This is called the **lepton** family (Table 2). By studying interactions involving the leptons, physicists were able to identify another conservation law. If all the leptons are given numbers (+1 for the electron and

Fig. 11 Conservation of lepton number

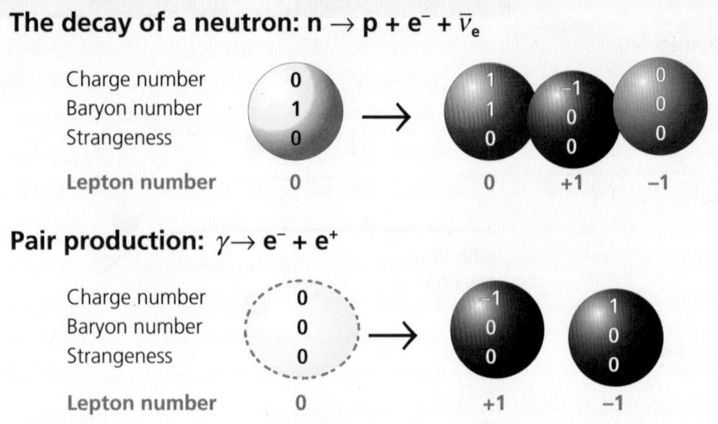

The decay of a neutron: $n \rightarrow p + e^- + \bar{v}_e$

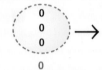

Charge number	0	1	-1	0
Baryon number	1	1	0	0
Strangeness	0	0	0	0
Lepton number	0	0	+1	-1

Pair production: $\gamma \rightarrow e^- + e^+$

Charge number	0	-1	1
Baryon number	0	0	0
Strangeness	0	0	0
Lepton number	0	+1	-1

Table 2 Leptons

Lepton (lepton number +1)	Antilepton (lepton number −1)
electron, e^-	positron, e^+
muon, μ^-	antimuon, μ^+
tau, τ^-	antitau, τ^+
electron neutrino, v_e	$\bar{v}_e$
muon neutrino, v_μ	$\bar{v}_\mu$
tau neutrino, v_τ	$\bar{v}_\tau$

the neutrino, –1 for the positron and the antineutrino), then the total lepton number is always the same before and after an interaction. Lepton number, like the charge and baryon numbers, is always conserved (Fig. 12).

 11 Which of the following interactions do not conserve lepton number, and are therefore impossible?

a $\quad \mu^- \rightarrow e^- + \bar{v}_e + v_\mu$

b $\quad \pi^+ \rightarrow \mu^+ + v_\mu + v_e$

c $\quad \mu^- \rightarrow e^- + \bar{v}_e$

Key ideas

- Electrons, muons and neutrinos are examples of leptons.

- Leptons are particles which, like quarks, have no known internal structure.

The finished picture

In 1974, the 'charm' quark was discovered. In 1977, the 'bottom' quark was discovered. In February 1995, two teams (totalling 900 people) working at the Fermi National Accelerator Laboratory in the US announced that they had conclusively observed the sixth and final quark. It took so much longer to find, because it was so much more massive than anyone had guessed (Fig. 12).

Physicists are now content that they have a finished set of particles. Six quarks, six leptons, their antiparticles and the four exchange particles (now called bosons). This hasn't stopped the questions of course. After all, why is the top quark so massive? What causes mass anyway?

One problem that faces scientists at every step is 'what questions can I ask?'.

Some questions turn out to be non-sensical, others turn out to have no answer. Perhaps the key to success of Californian culture is that it is open to new ideas, new influences. Just occasionally in science, asking the weirdest questions will get you a useful answer. A weird answer, but still a useful one.

Fig. 12 The standard model

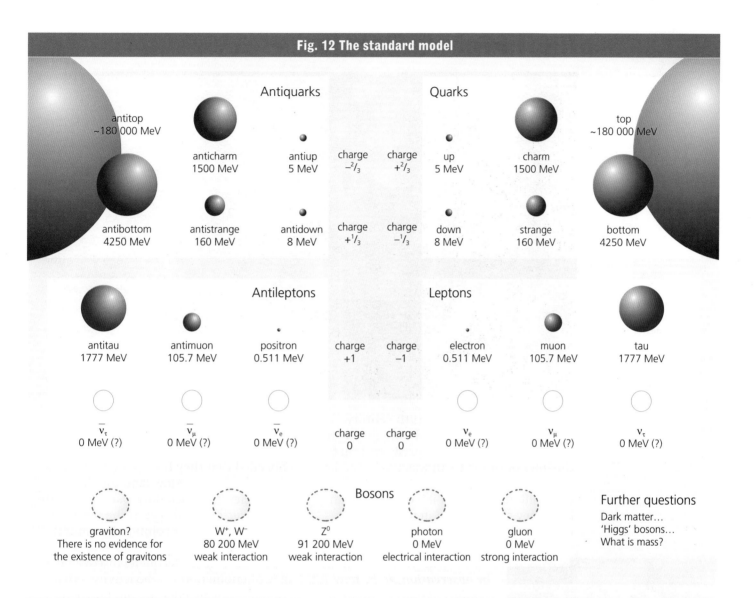

Antiquarks

			charge $-\frac{2}{3}$	charge $+\frac{2}{3}$			
	antitop ~180 000 MeV						top ~180 000 MeV
	anticharm 1500 MeV	antiup 5 MeV			up 5 MeV	charm 1500 MeV	
			charge $+\frac{1}{3}$	charge $-\frac{1}{3}$			
antibottom 4250 MeV	antistrange 160 MeV	antidown 8 MeV			down 8 MeV	strange 160 MeV	bottom 4250 MeV

Quarks

Antileptons

			charge +1	charge −1			
antitau 1777 MeV	antimuon 105.7 MeV	positron 0.511 MeV			electron 0.511 MeV	muon 105.7 MeV	tau 1777 MeV

Leptons

$\overline{\nu}_\tau$ 0 MeV (?)	$\overline{\nu}_\mu$ 0 MeV (?)	$\overline{\nu}_e$ 0 MeV (?)	charge 0	charge 0	ν_e 0 MeV (?)	ν_μ 0 MeV (?)	ν_τ 0 MeV (?)

Bosons

graviton? There is no evidence for the existence of gravitons	W^+, W^- 80 200 MeV weak interaction	Z^0 91 200 MeV weak interaction	photon 0 MeV electrical interaction	gluon 0 MeV strong interaction

Further questions
Dark matter…
'Higgs' bosons…
What is mass?

Fig. 13 Quark colour

Quarks have been given one more property – colour or 'colour charge'.
Quarks can have red, green or blue colour and only exist together in 'colourless' mixes:

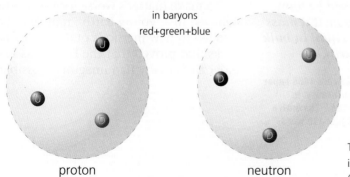

in baryons
red+green+blue

proton

neutron

in mesons
blue+antiblue
red+antired
green+antigreen

π^0 meson

The strong interaction felt by particles composed of quarks (hadrons) is carried between the quarks by exchange particles called gluons. (The pion exchange particle is a 'vehicle' for gluons.)

35

Radioactive Earth

The heat of creation? Physicists studied the rate of transfer of heat energy from inside the hot Earth and worked out how long ago the Earth was molten. But they were wrong.

In the second half of the 19th century, scientists clashed with each other over the age of the Earth. The physicists said that the interior of the Earth was too hot to be older than a few tens of millions of years – 400 million at most. If it were older than that, they claimed, its interior would be much cooler by now.

Sir William Thomson, better known as Lord Kelvin.

'...the heat which we know, by observation, to be now conducted out of the earth yearly is so great, that if this action had been going on with any approach to uniformity for 20,000 million years, the amount of heat lost ... would be more than enough to melt a mass of surface rock equal in bulk to the whole earth.'

Extract from Lord Kelvin's 1886 paper "The 'Doctrine of Uniformity' in Geology briefly refuted." The entire paper is made up of just 190 words and a calculation.

There seemed to be no flaws in the physicists' calculations, and many people accepted the answer. Most geologists conceded that they had to revise their view of continuous but slow land formation. Some scientists, including Darwin, saw this 'young Earth' as a threat to the newly developing idea of evolution by natural selection.

In 1895, Henri Becquerel discovered a new phenomenon – radioactivity – that seemed to create energy from nowhere. The Earth could have its own, previously unimagined, source of energy. Lord Kelvin's estimate was wrong. The Earth could be both old *and* hot because it had been kept 'on the boil' all the time.

To make matter's worse for those who believed in a 'young Earth', radioactivity also led to new methods of dating ancient rocks that proved that the Earth was vastly older than many had imagined possible.

4.1 Learning objectives

After working through this chapter, you should be able to:

- **describe** the different mechanisms of radioactive decay;

- **explain** the changes in atomic number and mass number that go with each of these decay processes;

- **relate** the stability of a nuclide to its size and to the ratio of its neutron number, N to its atomic number, Z;

- **write** nuclear reactions in a standard form;

- **represent** a radioactive decay chain both graphically and as a summary equation;

- **use** mass data to calculate the Q value of a given decay process;

- **explain** what is meant by the terms 'mass defect' (or 'mass difference') and 'binding energy'.

4.2 The energy of decay

Lord Kelvin's belief in a 'young Earth' really flew in the face of a large body of evidence accumulated by geologists. Unfortunately, physics is often viewed as the 'supreme' science. Had the study of geology been held in equal regard as physics, Kelvin may have pointed out that the Earth *must be* being kept warm by some as yet undiscovered process. His prior beliefs prevented him from taking this step. Not many years later, the discovery of radioactivity showed that there are processes which can continuously heat the inside of the Earth.

In radioactive decay, the total mass of the particles involved decreases. Mass and energy are interchangeable, and the mass that is lost during a radioactive decay is converted to energy. This energy takes the form of kinetic energy of the particles involved, and sometimes the energy of photons. The conversion factor, c^2 (equal to 9×10^{16} m^{2}s^{-2}), converts from units of kilograms to units of joules. The c^2 appears in the mass–energy formula, $E = mc^2$ (see *Physics Core* book, p. 164).

In practice, nuclear physicists do not often use the joule as their unit of energy because it is too big for measuring the energy of tiny particles. Instead they measure in **electronvolts**, eV, or in millions of electronvolts, MeV. In the same way, atomic mass units, u, are usually more suitable than kilograms. You can convert directly between MeV and u using a conversion factor of 931.3. One atomic mass unit is equivalent to an energy of 931.3 MeV.

This life-giving pacemaker is powered by the smallest of plutonium batteries. The energy from the radioactive decay produces enough electricity to run for years.

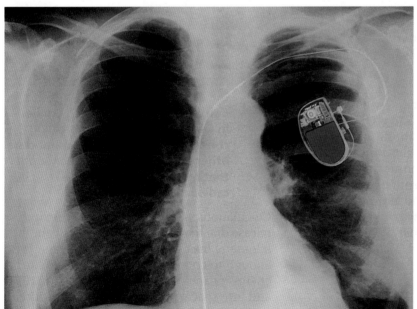

Table 1 Units of mass and energy		
Mass unit	**Conversion formula**	**Energy unit**
kg	$E = mc^2$	J
u	$E = 931.3\,u$	MeV

The amount of energy that is made available by the loss of mass in radioactive decay is called the **Q value** of the decay. This energy is divided up as kinetic energy in the emitted particles – the alpha and beta particles speed away – and kinetic energy in the nucleus, which recoils like a gun firing a bullet. Some of the energy is also used in the creation of massless particles such as neutrinos, antineutrinos and gamma photons.

Fig. 1 Radioactive decay

The decay of thallium-207 by β^- and γ emission:

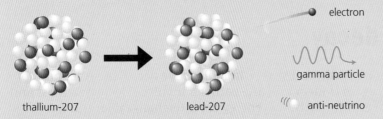

electron

gamma particle

thallium-207   lead-207   anti-neutrino

$$^{207}_{81}\text{Th} \rightarrow \,^{207}_{82}\text{Pb} + \,^{0}_{-1}\text{e} + \,\bar{\text{v}}_e + \gamma + Q$$

The thallium nucleus changes into a lead nucleus, emitting a beta (β^-) particle (an electron), an anti-neutrino and a gamma particle. The thallium is the **parent nucleus** and the lead is the **daughter nucleus**.

A β^- emission is always accompanied by the emission of an antineutrino, $\bar{\text{v}}_e$. The energy release, Q, includes not only the kinetic energy carried away by the particles, but also the energy required to create a gamma photon.

The decay of oxygen-13 by β^+ and proton emission:

$$^{13}_{8}\text{O} \rightarrow \,^{12}_{6}\text{C} + \,^{1}_{1}\text{p} + \,^{0}_{1}\text{e} + \,\text{v}_e + Q$$

Emission of a nucleon (a proton in this case) is quite rare.

Calculating Q

When uranium-238 decays by alpha emission, $^{238}_{92}\text{U} \rightarrow \,^{234}_{90}\text{Th} + \,^{4}_{2}\alpha + Q$, the nucleus changes into a thorium nucleus and the 92 electrons in the atom remain in place. This is two electrons too many, as a neutral thorium atom contains only 90 electrons. From this, and atomic mass data (see the Data section), we can deduce the mass change and the energy liberated (the Q value).

Mass of nuclear reactants:	*Mass of nuclear products:*
atom of uranium-238 = 238.05082 u	atom of thorium-234 = 234.04364 u
	two extra electrons = 2 m_e
	alpha particle = atom of helium – two electrons = 4.00260 u – 2 m_e

Total mass 'lost' = 238.05082 u –
234.04364 u – 2 m_e –
(4.00260 u – 2 m_e)
= 0.00458 u

Q value   = 0.00458 × 931.3
= 4.3 MeV

1   Iron-55 decays by electron capture – the nucleus absorbs one of its atom's electrons and a proton becomes a neutron. (Use the Data section)
   a Write out the nuclear reaction.
   b Is the daughter nucleus produced as a neutral atom or as an ion?
   c Calculate the Q value for this decay.

2   In a neutral atom of carbon-14, the nucleus decays by beta-emission. (Use the Data section)
   a Write out the nuclear reaction.
   b Is the daughter nucleus produced as a neutral atom or as an ion?
   c Calculate the Q value for this decay.

3   Rubidium-87 decays to strontium-87 by beta decay. (Use the Data section.)
Calculate the rate of energy release, in watts, in a specimen of rock containing 10 g of rubidium (and no other unstable nuclides). Remember that not all of the rubidium is radioactive.

Calculations show that the rate of energy release due to radioactive decay per cubic kilometre inside the Earth is significant. It is enough to compensate for the rate at which energy escapes through the Earth's surface and into space. Radioactive decay provides the Earth with its own energy source.

The discovery of radioactivity gave the geologists the time they needed – billions of years in which the Earth's rock could crystallise and remelt, wrinkle and fold, wear away and build up new layers. The shape of the ground that barely changes in a human lifetime was now seen to be just the present state of an ever-changing landscape.

It took many thousands of years for these folds to form. Geologists faced with a 'young Earth' had suggested that there had been periods of catastrophe in the past during which the land had rapidly changed. Now we know that most of the change is gradually accumulated over enormous stretches of time.

Key ideas

- Radioactive decays release energy.

- There are several modes of radioactive decay: α emission, β^- emission, β^+ emission, electron capture, nucleon emission and γ emission.

- Energy is made available by the destruction of mass, in accordance with Einstein's mass–energy formula, $E = mc^2$.

- The Q value of a particular decay can be calculated from the difference between the total mass of the particles before and after the decay.

4.3 Binding energy

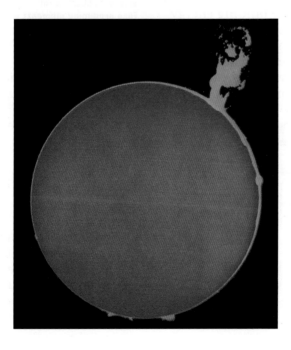

The Sun gets its energy by fusing small nuclei, or protons, together. This energy is the 'binding energy' of the new nuclei.

Before the possibility of mass–energy conversion had been considered, the Sun's source of energy had exercised a few imaginations. Wherever the energy was coming from, the fuel must be burning fast – so why wasn't it shrinking? Lord Kelvin suggested that the Sun got its energy from the gravitational potential energy of meteors collapsing and colliding, in which case it couldn't be much more than a few hundred million years old. This was another of Kelvin's less convincing arguments for a 'young Earth'.

Imagine a collection of free nucleons that come together to form a completely new nucleus. Like radioactive decay, the process would involve conversion of mass to energy. The nucleons would have less mass after getting together than they had before.

The mass lost – the difference between the total mass of the nucleons when they were free and the mass of the nucleus – is called the **mass defect** (or **mass difference**) of the nucleus.

Young stars, like our Sun, get their energy from the mass defects of helium nuclei:

Mass of a helium atom = 4.002603 u

A helium atom contains two electrons, so mass of helium nucleus = 4.002603 – 2 m_e

$$= 4.002603 \text{ u} - (2 \times 0.000549 \text{ u})$$
$$= 4.002603 \text{ u} - 0.001098 \text{ u}$$
$$= 4.001505 \text{ u}$$

Mass of 2 protons and 2 neutrons = 2 m_p + 2 m_n

$$= (2 \times 1.007276 \text{ u}) + (2 \times 1.008665 \text{ u})$$
$$= 2.014552 \text{ u} + 2.017330 \text{ u}$$
$$= 4.031882 \text{ u}$$

Mass defect = mass of free particles – mass of nucleus

$$= 4.031882 \text{ u} - 4.001505 \text{ u}$$
$$= 0.030377 \text{ u}$$

Should two protons and two neutrons join together, 0.03037 u of mass ceases to exist, and energy is made available. To break the nucleus apart again would require this energy to be paid back. The amount required to separate all the nucleons from a nucleus so that they become free neutrons and protons is called the **binding energy** of the nucleus (see *Physics Core* book, p. 164). The binding energy can also be thought of as the amount of energy that the nucleons give out when they first cluster together to form a nucleus.

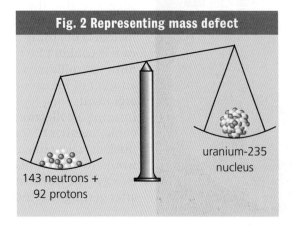

Fig. 2 Representing mass defect

143 neutrons + 92 protons

uranium-235 nucleus

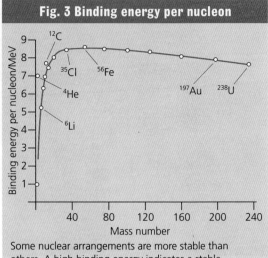

Fig. 3 Binding energy per nucleon

Some nuclear arrangements are more stable than others. A high binding energy indicates a stable arrangement. The helium nucleus is oddly stable.

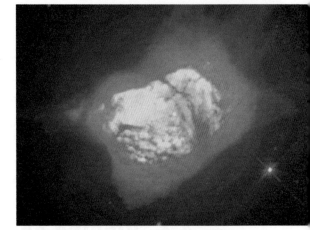

As a star uses up its initial hydrogen fuel, heavier elements start to form. The heavier elements start to fuse producing elements with less binding energy per nucleon – soaking up energy. Many really heavy elements only form in the catastrophic explosion of a dying star.

4 What is the binding energy of a helium nucleus?

5 Iron-56 is a very stable nucleus and is found at the core of stars. Calculate the energy that one kilogram of hydrogen fuel yields if it all ends up fused together as iron-56.

6a Compare the mass defects of lead-208 and lead-214.
 b Which has the greater binding energy per nucleon?
 c Which is more stable?

Key ideas

- The binding energy of a nucleus is the amount of energy that would be needed to separate all of its nucleons.

- The mass defect (or mass difference) of a nucleus is the mass that would need to be created in order for its nucleons to be separated.

- The binding energy and the mass defect are equivalent, linked by the mass–energy formula $E = mc^2$.

4.4 Age and abundance

'In molten rock, rubidium and strontium are usually spread out – separate from each other. But when it solidifies, the isotope of rubidium-87 continues decaying into strontium-87 and the two are found together – mother and daughter nuclei frozen in the same bit of rock.

In archaeology, we use the ratio of strontium-87 to rubidium-87 in a rock to show how long the strontium has been accumulating. This tells us how long the rock has been solid.'

Geological dating is commonly done by measuring the proportion of a nuclide to its decay product trapped in a rock. Rubidium-87 decays into stable strontium-87, and a simple measurement of their relative abundance in a sample is a tell-tale sign of the rock's age (Fig. 4).

Samples of uranium ore. Uranium is still found on Earth. It is the least unstable uranium isotopes that have survived.

With other nuclides such as uranium-238, this simple process is complicated by the fact that all nuclides heavier than lead-208 are, to some extent, unstable. Uranium-238 does not decay to a stable nuclide. In fact a uranium nucleus must go through no less than 14 decays before it becomes a stable nucleus (lead-206). This series of decays is called a **decay chain** (Fig. 5).

Most of the nuclides in the decay chain that runs from uranium-238 to lead-206 have half lives of a few seconds, a few minutes, or a few days. The most stable of them has a half life which is more than 10 000 times shorter than the half life of uranium-238. So all of these nuclides are only present in tiny amounts in uranium bearing rock. The overall process is a slow decrease in the proportion of uranium-238 relative to lead-206.

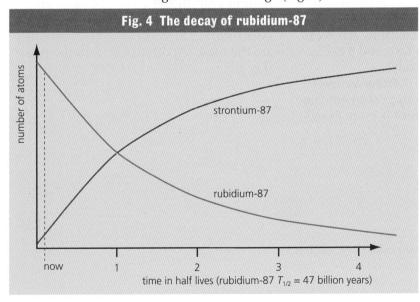

Fig. 4 The decay of rubidium-87

number of atoms

strontium-87

rubidium-87

now   1   2   3   4

time in half lives (rubidium-87 $T_{1/2}$ = 47 billion years)

Fig. 5 The uranium-238 decay chain

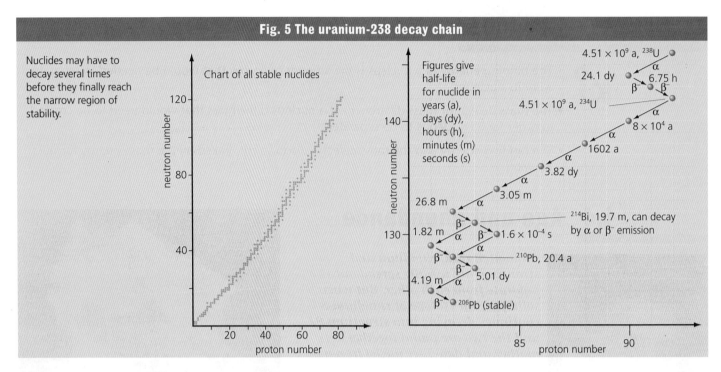

Nuclides may have to decay several times before they finally reach the narrow region of stability.

Chart of all stable nuclides

Figures give half-life for nuclide in years (a), days (dy), hours (h), minutes (m) seconds (s)

4.51×10^9 a, ^{238}U

24.1 dy   6.75 h

4.51×10^9 a, ^{234}U

8×10^4 a

1602 a

3.82 dy

3.05 m

26.8 m

^{214}Bi, 19.7 m, can decay by α or β^- emission

1.82 m 1.6×10^{-4} s

^{210}Pb, 20.4 a

4.19 m   5.01 dy

^{206}Pb (stable)

 7 One of the nuclides in the decay chain that starts with uranium-238 is polonium-214. This has a half life of 1.64×10^{-4} s.

a Comment on the likely abundance of this nuclide in a sample of rock that holds uranium.

b Sketch a graph to show the change in abundance of uranium-238 in the rock with time.

8 a Draw the graph of N vs Z (Fig. 5) and sketch in the zone of nuclear stability.

b Mark on cobalt-60. Draw arrows to indicate a decay by α and β decay. Which is more likely?

c Mark on carbon-9. Draw arrows to indicate a decay by proton emission and β^- decay. Which is more likely?

Radioactive dating with uranium–lead is essentially similar to dating with rubidium–strontium. Moon rocks and many meteorites have been dated by the uranium–lead method. No matter what method is used though, the same result keeps turning up each time – the rock seems to have been solid for 4.6 billion years. If the Moon, the meteorites and the Earth all formed at about the same time, then the Earth is also 4.6 billion years old. This stands in huge contrast to the 100 million years imagined by Lord Kelvin.

The immensity of the Earth's age is disconcerting if you believe that humans are the most important thing on the planet (Fig. 6).

Key ideas

• Nuclides decay in a chain until they reach a stable state.

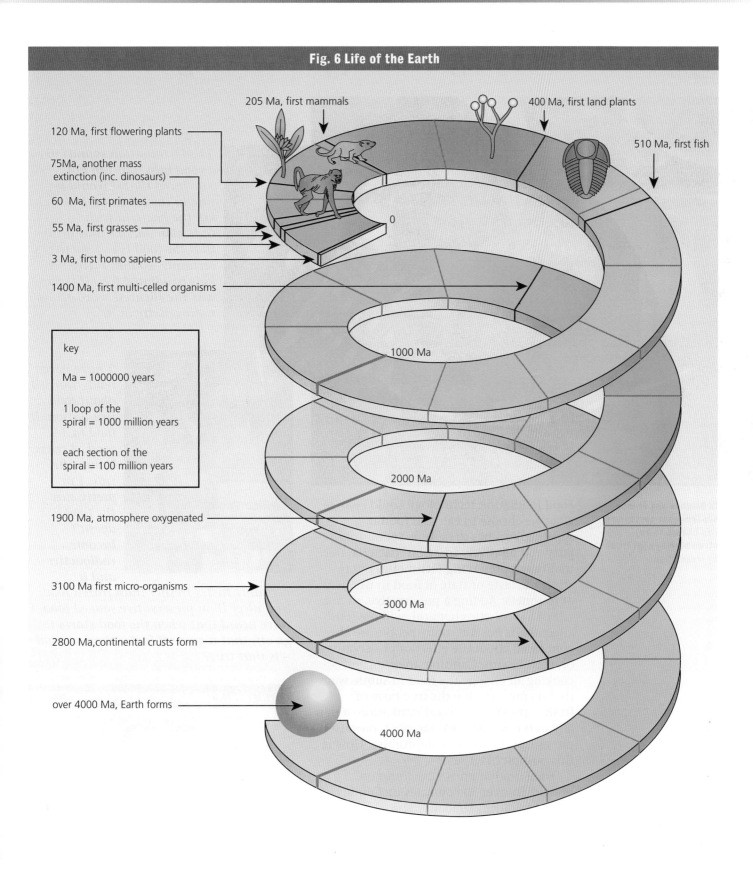

Fig. 6 Life of the Earth

205 Ma, first mammals

120 Ma, first flowering plants

400 Ma, first land plants

510 Ma, first fish

75Ma, another mass extinction (inc. dinosaurs)

60 Ma, first primates

55 Ma, first grasses

3 Ma, first homo sapiens

0

1400 Ma, first multi-celled organisms

key

Ma = 1000000 years

1 loop of the spiral = 1000 million years

each section of the spiral = 100 million years

1000 Ma

2000 Ma

1900 Ma, atmosphere oxygenated

3100 Ma first micro-organisms

3000 Ma

2800 Ma,continental crusts form

over 4000 Ma, Earth forms

4000 Ma

Decaying atoms, preserving food

'Food irradiation sounds like a good idea, but I'm not convinced that it would be safe in the long run. If you kill the bacteria with radiation doesn't that mean that the food is radioactive? I certainly wouldn't give my kids irradiated food if there was the slightest trace of radioactivity in it.'

'I have never really worried about food irradiation. If food tastes good, I guess it must be safe. I'm pretty sure the food doesn't become radioactive – and it certainly tastes fresher than frozen food and nicer than preservative soaked food. I have heard that when the food starts to go off, that it goes off faster than normal – is that true?'

In Belgium and France supermarket customers can choose to buy strawberries kept fresh by irradiation.

Food irradiation technology could change what we choose to eat. The food in supermarkets has to be kept appetising, tasty and relatively free from bacteria, but traditional preserving techniques often affect the taste or state of food in the name of freshness. Adding a preservative, such as salt or a synthetic chemical, will obviously affect the taste, and many people are also concerned about the effect of preservatives on their health. Canning, freezing and cooking all change the food in subtle ways that do not preserve the true taste of freshly grown food. Food irradiation, a new ally in the war against microbes, promises preservation without compromise. How is this possible? Is it safe?

Food irradiation is now common practice in over 30 countries including Canada, France, Thailand, The Netherlands, Norway and the USA. In the UK, many consumers are still uncertain about the safety of exposing food to radiation and it is going to take a lot more than a bowl of sweet fresh strawberries to convince them.

Fig. 1 Marking irradiated food

This symbol indicates that a food product has been treated with ionising radiation.

5.1 Learning objectives

After working through this chapter, you should be able to:

- **explain** the link between the different penetrating and ionising properties of alpha, beta and gamma radiations;

- **describe**, qualitatively, how and why parallel beams of alpha and beta radiations decline in intensity with their distance from their source;

- **predict**, quantitatively, the intensity of a parallel beam of gamma radiation at given distances in given media;

- **explain** the different energy spectra of alpha, beta and gamma emissions, and the role of 'tunnelling' in alpha emission;

- **outline** the principles of the experimental study of alpha and beta particle absorption.

5.2 Using radiation

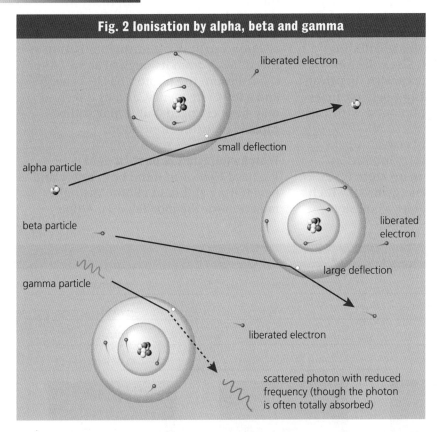

Fig. 2 Ionisation by alpha, beta and gamma

- liberated electron
- alpha particle
- small deflection
- beta particle
- liberated electron
- large deflection
- gamma particle
- liberated electron
- scattered photon with reduced frequency (though the photon is often totally absorbed)

How does radiation affect food? 'Radiation' should more fully be called 'ionising radiation' (Fig. 2). In food, as in any other organic material, ionisation affects the chemical bonding within molecules. Large doses of ionising radiation can disrupt the normal chemical behaviour of cells and kill living organisms, including microbes. That is the basis of food irradiation as a preservation technique. But how do we decide which sort of ionising radiation, if any, is best suited to this process.

Alpha radiation

Alpha radiation is highly ionising. Alpha particles are identical to helium nuclei. They have strong electric fields, which makes their interactions with electrons very frequent. Alpha particles are also quite massive, so they can rip an electron out of an atom without themselves being knocked off course.

Alpha particles lose a small proportion of their kinetic energy with each collision they make – a typical ionisation requires about 10 eV (**electronvolts**) of energy. The alpha particles continue to ionise until they lose all of their kinetic energy, then they continue their existence as ordinary helium nuclei, sooner or later finding free electrons and becoming neutral atoms. Because they ionise so easily and run out of energy, alpha particles do not penetrate deeply into materials – they couldn't make it from one side of a strawberry to the other.

It is important to remember that alpha emitting nuclides are extremely hazardous to handle. They are safe a few centimetres from the body, but if they come into contact with the body, for instance if traces are swallowed or breathed in, then they can cause a great deal of ionisation in the tissue in which they are absorbed.

 1 The total energy release of an alpha emission event is usually in the region of 5 MeV, and the alpha particle takes the bigger share of this energy. Estimate the number of ionisation events that a typical alpha particle will cause before it runs out of kinetic energy.

Beta radiation

Beta particles are less ionising and much less massive than alpha radiation. A typical beta particle might have an energy of 1 MeV (mega-electronvolts). Beta particles are identical to electrons – so when they cause ionisation, by dislodging electrons from neutral atoms with their strong electric field, they are colliding with identical particles. The collision between identical particles with identical masses means that ionising beta particles can be thrown widely off course with each collision.

Not every encounter between a beta particle and an atom causes ionisation. Sometimes an electron in an atom is knocked into a higher energy level, which *excites* the atom. Sometimes a collision results only in the recoil of an atom. These two processes transfer comparatively little energy from the beta particle. Therefore, a beta particle experiences many collisions of all three types, following an erratic path that turns with every collision, before its energy is all lost and it stops.

Gamma radiation

Gamma radiation consists of high-energy 'particles' of electromagnetic radiation, or high-energy **photons**. Photons, have no charge and no electric field, so interactions with electrons in atoms are comparatively rare. A photon can travel many centimetres through a low density medium like air before it induces any ionisation.

When a gamma photon does make a direct hit on an electron in an atom, a proportion of the photon's energy is transferred to the electron, firstly as potential energy to liberate the electron and secondly as kinetic energy. (The electron might cause further ionisation as it speeds away from its original atom.) After the collision, the photon has less energy and a lower frequency, and its direction may have changed, but it may still be capable of further ionisation.

Which radiation is best to use?

We need to bear in mind both safety and penetrating ability to choose the right radiation for the job (Table 1). Alpha

Table 1 Characteristics of ionising radiation			
ionising particle	alpha	beta	gamma
ionising strength	very strong	strong	weak
typical energy	5MeV	1MeV	10MeV
penetrating ability (stopped by)	mm of paper/skin	mm of aluminium	m of lead
cloud chamber tracks			

particles are not suitable for food irradiation because the sources are hazardous to handle and it is difficult to give an even, measured dose of radiation to the food because of their poor penetrating ability. Both beta and gamma particles have good penetrating abilities, making them ideal for delivering an even, measured dose, but are they safe to use?

An electron beam from an accelerator, such as an electron gun, is much safer and cheaper than a beta source. The energy of electrons from an electron gun can match that of beta particles. The voltage applied to the electrodes of the machine is the deciding factor. A 1 MV potential difference will provide each electron with an energy of 1 MeV – the energy of a typical beta particle.

Electron guns can also produce X-rays, with frequencies from 10^{17} to 10^{21} Hz (Fig. 3). Here, the electrons do not make contact with the food, but collide with a metal target, where their rapid deceleration results in X-ray emission. The ionising and penetrating properties of X-rays are exactly the same as those of gamma rays (Fig. 4). In fact, some gamma rays are identical to X-rays, with frequencies down to about 10^{19} Hz, but gamma rays come from radioactive sources.

Q 2a Write down the masses and charges of alpha and beta particles.

  b Explain why beta particles are more penetrative than alpha particles which have the same initial energy.

3a Calculate the energy, in eV, of a 10^{18} Hz gamma photon. Use $E = hf$ and 1 eV = 1.6×10^{-19} J.

  b If all of the energy of this photon is transferred to the kinetic energy of an electron, estimate the speed of the electron.

  c Explain why gamma radiation induces ionisation comparatively rarely.

4 Explain why alpha particles leave strong straight tracks in a cloud chamber, beta particle leave very faint tracks with randomly changing direction, and gamma rays leave almost no tracks at all.

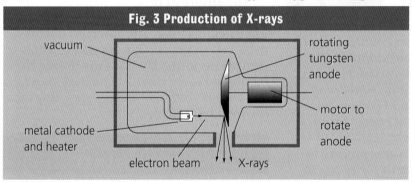

Fig. 3 Production of X-rays

vacuum

rotating tungsten anode

motor to rotate anode

metal cathode and heater

electron beam   X-rays

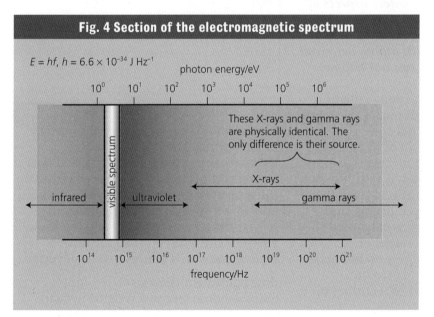

Fig. 4 Section of the electromagnetic spectrum

$E = hf$, $h = 6.6 \times 10^{-34}$ J Hz^{-1}

photon energy/eV

10^0 10^1 10^2 10^3 10^4 10^5 10^6

These X-rays and gamma rays are physically identical. The only difference is their source.

X-rays

infrared | visible spectrum | ultraviolet | gamma rays

10^{14} 10^{15} 10^{16} 10^{17} 10^{18} 10^{19} 10^{20} 10^{21}

frequency/Hz

It would seem that both beta and gamma radiation are suitable for destroying bacteria in food. But radiation causes ionisation that can affect the complex molecules in both bacteria *and* food. For example, it reduces the vitamin content of food, but no more so than other preserving techniques like freezing or cooking. It can affect the taste of food, especially food with a high fat content, so food irradiation is regarded as inappropriate for preserving dairy products or meat.

5.3 Ensuring safety

'The food here at Isotron is irradiated largely for export to other countries that allow the widespread consumption of irradiated foods. We follow strict guidelines from the EC and Ministry of Agriculture, Fisheries and Food on the allowed dose of radiation energy for each food type.
We have been using the same process to sterilise medical equipment for years, so we are well aware of the safety aspects of working with radiation. People seem to imagine that irradiating the food must make it radioactive. With alpha, beta and gamma radiations this can not happen.'

Neither alpha, beta nor gamma radiation interact significantly with nuclei, except to make them recoil after collisions. A photon, once it has lost all of its energy through causing ionisation, ceases to exist – without energy, a photon is nothing. Alpha and beta particles also transfer their energy through ionising collisions, and when their kinetic energy is exhausted they exist as ordinary helium nuclei or electrons. Ionising radiations do not make nuclei radioactive, and they do not themselves survive as harmful entities in the material.

The only atomic particles that can fundamentally change nuclei are free neutrons. Free neutrons can enter nuclei, increasing their mass. The new nucleus may not be a stable isotope of the element.

So neutrons are capable of making material become radioactive. Neutrons are therefore unsuitable for food irradiation and a beam of neutrons is *very* hazardous.

An acceptable dose

The microbes living on food that is irradiated are killed because the ionising radiation has enough energy to disrupt the chemistry of the living cell. The chemical products of the ionising radiation are termed 'radiolytic products' and are in all cases identical, or similar, to products resulting from cooking and other preservation techniques.

The **absorbed dose** of radiation is the energy absorbed in joules per kilogram of irradiated material. The absorbed dose is measured in **grays** (Gy). Food irradiation regulations in the UK limit the dosage to food to no more than 10 kilograys (kGy), but outlines different doses depending on the food type (Table 2).

Table 2 Allowable absorbed dose for food irradiation in the UK	
fruit	2 kGy
vegetables	1 kGy
bulbs and tubers	0.2 kGy
spices	10 kGy
fish	3 kGy
poultry	7 kGy

When considering the energy absorbed by human beings from ionising radiation, we are more concerned with the *type* of damage it can do. A better way to assess the effect on the human body is to multiply the absorbed dose of energy by a weighting factor that reflects the type of radiation and the tissue affected. The result is called the **dose equivalent** which is measured in **sieverts**:

dose equivalent (sieverts) =
absorbed dose (grays) × weighting factor

The weighting factor (sometimes called the quality factor, Q, or the relative biological effectiveness) ranges from 20, for very harmful alpha radiation, down to 1, for gamma and beta radiation.

The average background radiation in the UK has the energy to give you a few thousandths of a sievert each year (Fig. 5). It is worth remembering that 12% of the background radiation you receive comes from natural material ingested by eating, drinking and breathing (Fig. 6).

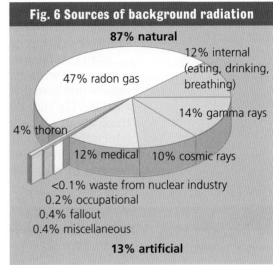

Fig. 6 Sources of background radiation

87% natural

47% radon gas

12% internal (eating, drinking, breathing)

14% gamma rays

4% thoron

12% medical

10% cosmic rays

<0.1% waste from nuclear industry
0.2% occupational
0.4% fallout
0.4% miscellaneous

13% artificial

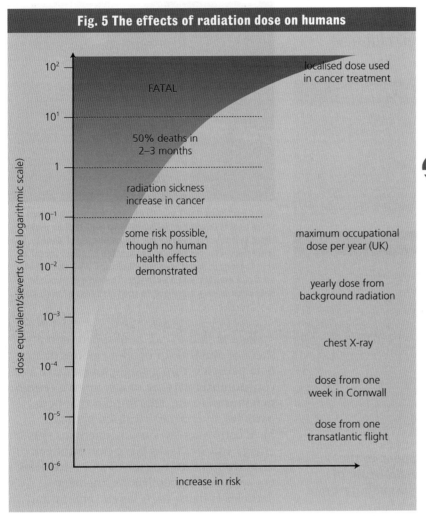

Fig. 5 The effects of radiation dose on humans

dose equivalent/sieverts (note logarithmic scale)

10^2 — FATAL — localised dose used in cancer treatment

10^1

1 — 50% deaths in 2–3 months

10^{-1} — radiation sickness increase in cancer

10^{-2} — some risk possible, though no human health effects demonstrated — maximum occupational dose per year (UK)

10^{-3} — yearly dose from background radiation

10^{-4} — chest X-ray

10^{-5} — dose from one week in Cornwall

10^{-6} — dose from one transatlantic flight

increase in risk

5 Here are three newspaper headlines written by journalists who know very little physics:
'Food contains radiation!'
'Food contaminated by exposure to radiation!'
'Food contaminated by traces of radioactive material!'
Comment on each headline.

6a Use the Data section to select a suitable radionuclide for use for food irradiation. Take account of such factors as the type of emission, the initial activity of the material, its useful lifetime, and problems of disposal when it is no longer of use.

b How would you ensure that there was no possibility of small quantities of the material contaminating food?

5.4 Spreading, absorption and intensity

For all types of radiation (ionising or not), the rate at which energy flows through a unit of cross sectional area (the intensity), decreases with distance from a source. For example, light spreading from a small source in a vacuum follows an inverse square law – the intensity of light is inversely proportional to the square of the distance from the source (Fig. 7). Put simply, the light intensity becomes weaker as it spreads out. For *ionising* radiation travelling in a real substance, not only does the radiation spread out (*dissipation*), but loss of energy by ionisation (*absorption*) plays a very significant part in determining intensity.

With two factors involved the variation of intensity with distance from its source is more complicated than for light in a vacuum. For simplicity, it is worthwhile to think about a parallel beam of radiation, in which there is no dissipation at all (Fig. 8). The graph shows how radiation intensity behaves in such a simplified situation (Fig. 9).

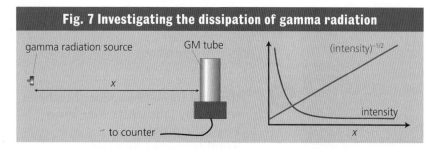

Fig. 7 Investigating the dissipation of gamma radiation

gamma radiation source

GM tube

x

to counter

(intensity)$^{-1/2}$

intensity

x

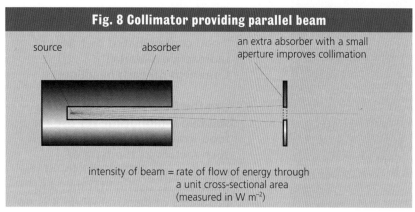

Fig. 8 Collimator providing parallel beam

source

absorber

an extra absorber with a small aperture improves collimation

intensity of beam = rate of flow of energy through a unit cross-sectional area (measured in W m^{-2})

7 Explain what happens to the intensity of a *parallel* beam of visible radiation spreading from a source,

a **in a vacuum,**

b **in clean air,**

c **in foggy, or polluted, air.**

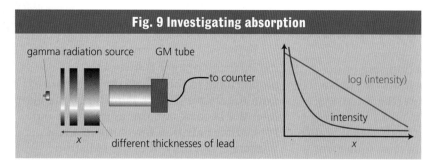

Fig. 9 Investigating absorption

gamma radiation source

GM tube

to counter

x

different thicknesses of lead

log (intensity)

intensity

x

Characteristics of absorption

Alpha particles from a single source travel for one of a small number of short discrete distances – you can see this in the tracks in a cloud chamber. This implies that the alpha particles emerge from the nucleus with one of a small number of discrete energies.

Alpha particles don't penetrate very far which makes them unsuitable for irradiating food, but it does make them suitable for measuring the thickness of sheet materials. The continuous production of sheet metal at this factory is monitored for thickness with the aid of an alpha emitter and a detector. The rate of particle detection is very sensitive to the thickness of material.

Beta radiation can be stopped with a sheet of aluminium or a few metres of air. Beta particles from a single source have a continuously varying range, up to a certain maximum, in air. This implies that beta particles, in contrast to alpha particles, have continuously varying energies. This energy transfer takes place over a longer distance than in the case of alpha particles, but with enough collisions, the beta particles exhaust their kinetic energy and come to a stop.

Gamma photons are very different – they lose a large proportion of their energy, sometimes all of it, in a single ionisation. One by one, as if at random, photons lose their energy to the medium they are moving through and cease to exist. The material absorbs the photons. The more photons there are in a beam, the more absorption there is taking place – the absorption of a parallel gamma beam (that is the *change* in intensity) is proportional to its intensity:

change of intensity $\propto$ – intensity

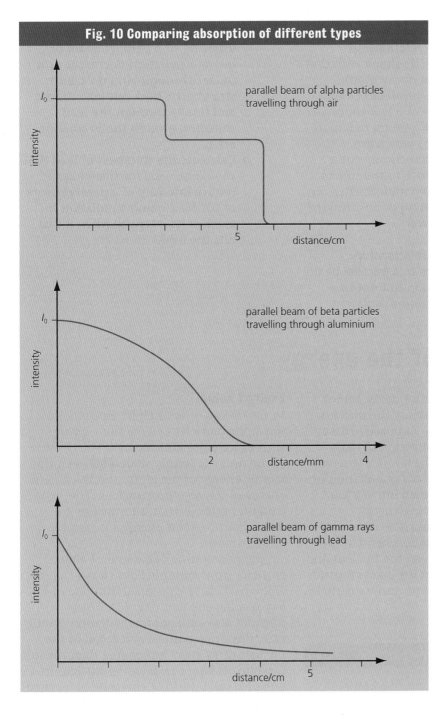

Fig. 10 Comparing absorption of different types

parallel beam of alpha particles travelling through air

intensity / distance/cm

parallel beam of beta particles travelling through aluminium

intensity / distance/mm

parallel beam of gamma rays travelling through lead

intensity / distance/cm

The minus sign is necessary because intensity is positive but the change is negative. With I for intensity and c as a constant, this becomes:

$$\frac{\mathrm{d}I}{\mathrm{d}x} = -cI$$

When the change of a quantity is proportional to its own value the result is an exponential change (Fig. 10):

$$I = I_0 \times e^{-cx}$$

Where I_0 is the initial value of the intensity. (Compare this with capacitor discharge, change of an unchecked population in biology, and with radioactive decay.) The constant c is called the **attenuation coefficient** of the medium, written as μ:

$$I = I_0 \times e^{-\mu x}$$

Note that in a vacuum, there is no absorption, and the intensity of a parallel beam is constant however far it travels. The attenuation coefficient is then zero.

Gamma rays, or high energy X-rays, are weakly ionising but highly penetrating. For food irradiation, the weak ionisation makes it necessary to use a high intensity beam, but the high penetration means that a large thickness of food receives exposure to the same level of radiation. The food absorbs only a small proportion of the initial intensity of a beam, so an irradiation plant needs heavy shielding made from a good absorber, usually lead.

The radiographers taking this X-ray wear protective aprons to protect them from repeated exposure. They only take the X-ray when they are behind the protective screen.

Table 3 Values of gamma attenuation coefficient (μ) in cm^{-1}

Photon energy/MeV	0.05	0.40	10.00
air	2.64×10^{-4}	1.24×10^{-4}	0.26×10^{-4}
water	0.221	0.106	0.022
lead	97.75	2.53	0.58

8a Sketch an inverse square law graph representing the relationship $I = k/x^2$. Compare its shape with that of an exponential decay graph.

b What is the absorption effect on gamma radiation of a few cm of air?

c A point source of gamma radiation produces photons which are spreading in all directions, not a parallel beam. Close to the source, which is the dominant influence on intensity – spreading or absorption? Explain your answer.

9 Explain why the relationship $I = I_0 \times e^{-\mu x}$ applies to a parallel beam of gamma radiation but not to a parallel beam of alpha radiation.

10a Sketch a graph to show how intensity of a parallel beam of gamma radiation decreases as it passes through air, into a 2 cm strawberry, back out into the air, and finally through the lead shielding around the irradiation area.

b Calculate the thickness of lead that should be used for shielding to reduce intensity of a parallel beam of 0.4 MeV gamma radiation to 0.1% of its intensity when it first hits the lead.

5.5 The source of the energy

The energy from radioactive decay comes from one source – the mass of the nucleus. The creation of energy in radioactive decay is accompanied by a destruction of mass. This is the reason why the law of conservation of mass and the law of conservation of energy have to be combined into a a joint law of conservation of mass–energy.

When a nucleus decays, the liberated energy of the transformation, termed the **Q value**, is shared between the nucleus and any ejected particles. Yet the characteristic energies of alpha, beta and gamma particles are very different.

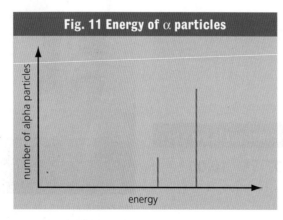

Fig. 11 Energy of α particles

number of alpha particles

energy

Excited nuclei

In the decays of *some* alpha emitters, all of the alpha particles emerge from a sample with exactly the same energy. The Q value of the decay is simply shared between the kinetic energy of the alpha and the kinetic energy of the recoiling nucleus. The daughter nucleus that is formed by the decay has no excess energy – it is in its 'ground state'.

The penetrating behaviour of alpha particles from *most* nuclides shows that the alpha particles are grouped into one of a few specific energies (Fig. 11). These nuclides also emit gamma radiation. In this case, the alpha particle and recoil of the nucleus carry away less energy than the full Q value, leaving the daughter nucleus in one of several possible energetic or 'excited' states. Sooner rather than later, the nucleus gets rid of the excess energy by emitting a gamma ray photon (Fig. 12).

11 Calculate the possible gamma ray photon frequencies emitted from a sample of caesium-137 (use Fig. 12).

Fig. 12 Nuclear energy levels in Cs-137

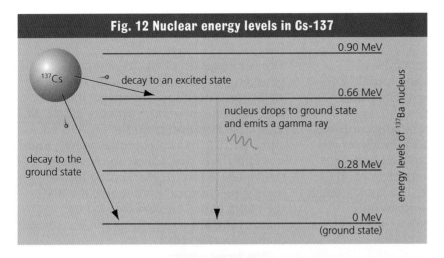

^{137}Cs

0.90 MeV

decay to an excited state

0.66 MeV

nucleus drops to ground state
and emits a gamma ray

0.28 MeV

decay to the
ground state

energy levels of ^{137}Ba nucleus

0 MeV
(ground state)

Fig. 13 Energy of β particles

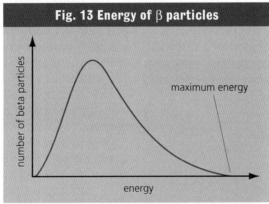

number of beta particles

maximum energy

energy

Fig. 14 Particle explosion

For two particles, the energy and momentum of one particle determines the energy and momentum of the other particle.

With three particles, the energy and momentum of the second and third particles can be shared any number of ways.

Fig. 15 neutrino and antineutrino

 v $\bar{v}$

Millions of neutrinos from the Sun pass through your body every second with no effect at all. In fact they are still passing through your body at night, up through your bed, because neutrinos 'shine' straight through the Earth unaffected.
Neutrinos are still something of a mystery to scientists. They are unaffected by both electrical and gravitational fields, so they have little or no mass and no electrical charge. Neutrinos have energy and a property called 'spin'. The main difference between a neutrino and its antiparticle (an antineutrino) is the direction of the spin.

Wolfgang Pauli who won the Nobel Prize in 1945.

The beta energy spectrum

Energy spectra for beta particles could not be more different from the energy spectra of alpha particles. Observations of beta decay show that energy of beta particles varies, from zero up to the total Q value of the particular decay (Fig. 13). One is continuous and the other is discrete. This presented a puzzle when scientists first observed it – why should beta emission be different from alpha emission? It took some imaginative thinking from the Austrian physicist Wolfgang Pauli to come up with a possible answer: the presence, in beta decay, of an *undetected* third particle.

Two particles emerging from an explosion can only share momentum and energy in one way. Momentum has to be conserved, so the particles fly apart along a straight line with velocities given by:

$$m_1v_1 + m_2v_2 = 0$$

Energy has to be conserved:

$$\tfrac{1}{2}m_1v_1^2 + \tfrac{1}{2}m_2v_2^2 = \text{energy of explosion.}$$

If you know the values of m_1 and m_2 that only leaves two unknowns: v_1 and v_2. With two equations to work from, you can find the value of two unknowns. In this case you can substitute the value of v_1:

$$v_1 = -\frac{m_2v_2}{m_1}$$

into the second equation to give a unique value for v_1. With one extra variable and still only two equations, there can be many different solutions. Three particles can therefore fly apart in a range of different directions, sharing momentum and energy in a variety of ways (Fig. 14). Though there was no direct evidence for a third particle in beta decay, it did explain the continuous spectrum. Physicists supposed that the new particles were hard to detect because they had no mass and no charge but were just bundles of energy, rather like photons. They called them neutrinos and antineutrinos, and they became part of nuclear physics 25 years before they were actually detected.

Q12 **Explain why beta particle energy ranges up to a maximum value. (The maximum value is characteristic to each beta emitting nuclide.)**

53

5.6 The mystery of alpha decay

By considering the energy of decay, physicists had to invent an entirely new particle (the neutrino) to explain the behaviour of beta particles. This was quickly accepted and eventually confirmed by experiment. But a second problem was discovered: alpha particles simply do not have enough energy to escape from the nucleus in the first place. This took a much more drastic solution: particles must behave in previously unimagined ways.

Emission impossible

'Potential energy against distance graphs' are helpful in imagining the behaviour of an alpha particle in the region of a nucleus.

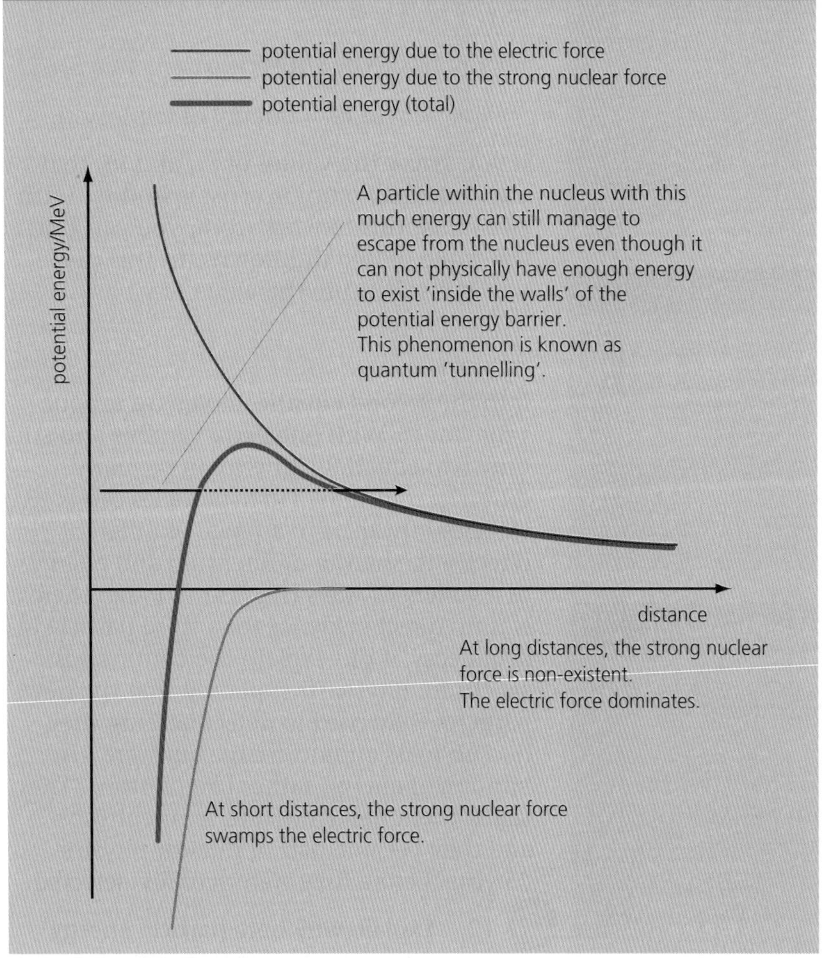

The combination of electrical repulsion between protons and the strong nuclear attraction determines the shape of the potential energy against distance graph. At very large distances from the nucleus an alpha particle has no potential energy, and it is effectively free. Closer to the nucleus, the repulsive electric forces produces an increasing electrical potential, but when the alpha particle is very close to the nucleus the attractive strong nuclear force dominates (Fig. 16).

Nucleons within a nucleus are not in a state of rest and four nucleons may occasionally come together for a while into a relatively stable cluster – an alpha particle within the nucleus. Only a small proportion of such clusters escape. Such escape is energetically very difficult because the alpha particle must cross the potential barrier.

Just as a truck on a roller-coaster ride needs enough kinetic energy to get over a rise in the track (a gravitational potential rise), you might imagine that an alpha particle must have enough kinetic energy to get into or out of the nucleus (an electrical potential rise). So most scientists would have believed at the beginning of the 20th century. But alpha particle emission is far more common than nineteenth century physics predicts.

It seems that an alpha particle *can* get out of the nucleus without ever gaining all of the energy needed to get to the top of the potential barrier. It is as if an alpha particle disappears from one side of the wall, tunnels through it, and reappears on the other side. It seems very strange, but there is no other explanation for the frequency with which alpha emission occurs. Physics can not ignore reality, and if that means abandoning comfortable 'common sense' ideas of how we would expect small particles to behave, then that is what we must do. In the microworld of nuclei, perhaps we should expect to be surprised.

Fig. 16 Potential energy of an α particle

—— potential energy due to the electric force
—— potential energy due to the strong nuclear force
—— potential energy (total)

potential energy/MeV

A particle within the nucleus with this much energy can still manage to escape from the nucleus even though it can not physically have enough energy to exist 'inside the walls' of the potential energy barrier.
This phenomenon is known as quantum 'tunnelling'.

distance

At long distances, the strong nuclear force is non-existent.
The electric force dominates.

At short distances, the strong nuclear force swamps the electric force.

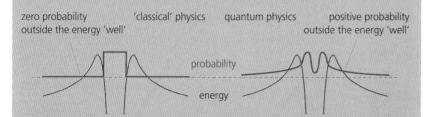

Fig. 17 Quantum tunnelling

zero probability outside the energy 'well' 'classical' physics   quantum physics   positive probability outside the energy 'well'

probability

energy

The branch of physics called 'Quantum Mechanics' does not treat particles as if they exist at a particular place – instead particles have a *probability* of being in any particular place.

Traditionally, the probability of a particle trapped inside a 'potential well' would drop to zero at the wall because the cluster does not have enough energy to move any further. The mathematics of Quantum Mechanics predicts a small but positive probability in the energetically 'impossible' zone. The tiny probability of existing outside the potential well means that every now and then the particle can miraculously find itself outside the potential well.

Another way of thinking about this 'quantum trick' is to imagine that the particle is able to 'borrow' some energy and pay it back very quickly.

This process of alpha escape, of their moving from one side of the potential barrier to the other, is called tunnelling.

13 a Use the height of the potential barrier shown in Fig. 16 to estimate the speed of an alpha particle cluster inside a nucleus that escapes by climbing over the potential barrier.

b Estimate the speed of an alpha particle cluster inside a nucleus that escapes by tunnelling.

5.7 Making decisions

People, largely unaware of the physical processes involved, are suspicious of ionising radiation and the use of irradiation. They would prefer their food to be uncomplicated by such technologies. People were initially wary of the use of microwave ovens because of similar concerns.

The fear that beta or gamma radiation can make food radioactive is based on a misunderstanding of the relationship between radioactivity and materials. Other objections have more credibility, such as the concern that irradiation could cause harmful chemical changes. Researchers all over the world, in well-designed and lengthy experiments, have not found any hazardous consequences of the substances created by exposing food to radiation.

The food industry looks at how the irradiation of medical equipment, such as syringes, has transformed routine work in the health industry. It sees benefits of cost and of food safety, and seems likely to continue to push for increase in food irradiation.

The WHO Golden Rules for Safe Food Preparation

1 – Choose foods processed for safety
While many foods, such as fruits and vegetables, are best in their natural state, others simply are not safe unless they have been processed. For example, always buy pasteurised as opposed to raw milk and, if you have the choice, select fresh or frozen poultry treated with ionising radiation.

Extract from World Health Organisation 'Golden Rules for Safe Food Preparation'.

A nuclear commitment

In Germany, opposition to nuclear power has been intense, with violent clashes between police and protesters.

THE MAGIC HANDS OF AMF
Harness The Atom For Peace

Atomic energy is a source of great hope for the future. It can supply useful power to help nations grow, and to help raise living standards in every land.

In more than 13 countries around the world AMF has already installed, or is presently building, nuclear research reactors for productive purposes.

These reactors, like so many AMF products, are Magic Hands that help take the drudgery out of life. Magic Hands that hold the key to many advances in science and medicine... that will open the door to a better life for everyone.

American Machine & Foundry Company, AMF Building, 261 Madison Avenue, New York 16, N. Y. Overseas plants and offices: Bologna · Geneva · London · Mexico City · San Juan · São Paulo Stockholm · Sydney · Tokyo · Wiesbaden

In the 1950s, scientists were convinced that a new era of cheap electricity had arrived.

In 1945, the French government set up the Commissariat à l'Energie Atomique. By the 1960s, France was capable of building its own nuclear bombs and nuclear power stations. In the early 1970s, the price of oil rose dramatically throughout the world. France had little coal and barely any oil or gas under its own soil – the French economy was at the mercy of the oil producers. The government decided to expand its nuclear programme – in a big way. French electricity generation from nuclear power stations increased from 8% (in the 1970s) to nearly 75% by the end of the 1980s (Fig. 1).

With their lack of fossil fuels, and their mountain rivers already heavily dammed for hydroelectric generation, the French have generally accepted the role of nuclear power in maintaining their prosperity. France's economy is supported by, and committed to, cheap electricity from its nuclear programme.

Elsewhere in the world, people were less enthusiastic about nuclear power. In referenda in Sweden and California, USA, voters instructed the politicians to phase out nuclear power.

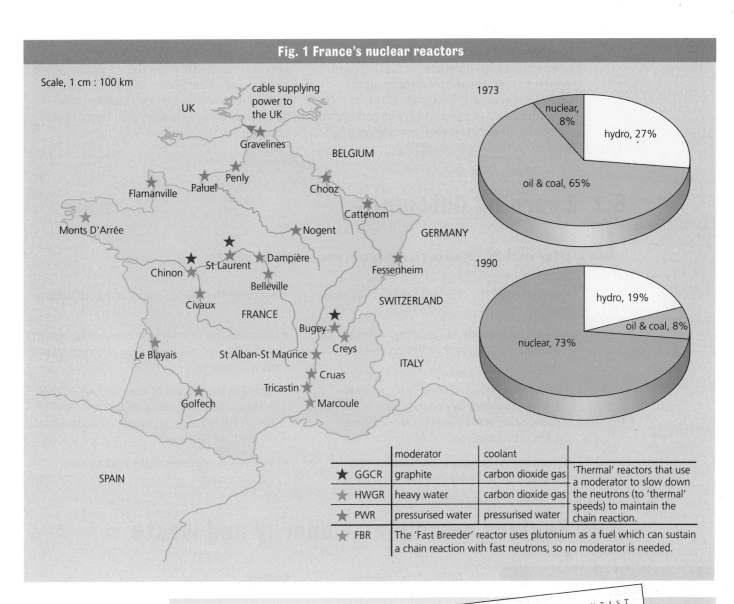

Fig. 1 France's nuclear reactors

Scale, 1 cm : 100 km

UK

cable supplying power to the UK

Gravelines

BELGIUM

Penly

Flamanville Paluel

Chooz

Monts D'Arrée

Cattenom

GERMANY

Nogent

Dampière

St Laurent

Chinon

Fessenheim

Belleville

SWITZERLAND

Civaux

FRANCE

Bugey

Le Blayais

St Alban-St Maurice

Creys

ITALY

Cruas

Tricastin

SPAIN

Golfech

Marcoule

1973

- nuclear, 8%
- hydro, 27%
- oil & coal, 65%

1990

- hydro, 19%
- oil & coal, 8%
- nuclear, 73%

		moderator	coolant	
★	GGCR	graphite	carbon dioxide gas	'Thermal' reactors that use a moderator to slow down the neutrons (to 'thermal' speeds) to maintain the chain reaction.
★	HWGR	heavy water	carbon dioxide gas	
★	PWR	pressurised water	pressurised water	
★	FBR	The 'Fast Breeder' reactor uses plutonium as a fuel which can sustain a chain reaction with fast neutrons, so no moderator is needed.		

The current controversy on waste storage divides experts in the UK.

NEW SCIENTIST

FOCUS

The longer nuclear waste is stored the greater the risk of a leak. But should the government be panicked into skipping a public inquiry into a permanent repository under Sellafield?

The battle of Britain's nuclear dustbin

Jeremy Webb

RADIOACTIVE waste frightens both the public and politicians like nothing else. So energy minister Tim Eggar cannot have welcomed the letter from John Horlock, one of the government's most senior advisers on nuclear safety, warning that the packaging of radioactive waste at some sites in Britain is "deteriorating" and "unsatisfactory for long-term storage". The longer this waste remains in this state, wrote Horlock, the bigger the danger of radiation leaks.

Horlock's answer is to short-circuit the process for approving the deep-level radioactive waste repository which Nirex

figures—for 1991—more than 51 500 cubic metres of waste is in store, enough to half fill the Albert Hall.

It is the state of this waste that concerns Horlock, who retired in September as head of the independent Advisory Committee on the Safety of Nuclear Installations. He bases his warning on two reports carried out by a working group of the advisory committee that assessed the state of the country's waste stores. He declines to discuss his letter until the second of these reports is published.

The first report examines British Nuclear Fuels' site at Sellafield. It says silos built in the 1960s to hold chunks of fuel cladding

Challenge over nuclear waste lab

CUMBRIA County Council called last week for a public inquiry into plans to build a radioactive waste dump beneath the nuclear complex at Sellafield. The council's request was prompted by a planning application by Nirex, Britain's nuclear waste disposal company, to excavate a rock laboratory 735 metres below ground.

Again in a few years, to repackage their waste increasing costs and the exposure of

The use of nuclear power has proved a source of emotive debate. It is an area in which scientists can not supply all the answers, because it involves so much more than the basic physics of power generation. But as in all debates, real developments lead from true understanding.

So what are the real risks at a nuclear power station? How do they compare with the risks of other forms of electricity generation? What can be done to make nuclear power even safer and more cost-effective?

6.1 Learning outcomes

After working through this chapter, you should be able to:

- **understand** the charged liquid drop model of fission;

- **describe** the role of neutrons in fission of a single nucleus and in fission chain reactions;

- **understand** that nuclear reactors make energy available by reducing the total mass of particles and increasing the binding energy per nucleon;

- **describe** the purpose and action of a moderator material in a thermal reactor;

- **describe** the purpose and action of control rods;

- **describe** the problems and possible benefits of the flow of neutrons that emerges from a nuclear reactor;

- **describe** the nature of reactor fuel, of the changes that take place to the fuel, and of the problems associated with the daughter products of fission;

- **review** the arguments for and against nuclear power.

6.2 Nuclear principles – energy and waste

'The bulk of the nuclear waste that we create at the power plant is low level – it even includes the disposable paper clothing that we wear.'

Energy

Uranium-235 is the fuel upon which French and other operating nuclear reactors depend. The **fission**, or splitting, of a nucleus of uranium-235 is triggered when it absorbs a neutron, turning briefly into a nucleus of uranium-236 which wobbles like a free-floating globule of liquid until it breaks into two parts (Fig. 2). The two new nuclei are called **daughter nuclei**.

Energy is made available because the total mass of the end products of fission is less than that of the initial particles. The mass–energy equation, $E = mc^2$ (where c is

This fuel element is packed with rods that contain pellets of uranium. It is fission of Uranium-235 that keeps a reactor going. This fuel element is submerged in water. The blue glow is caused by energetic particles travelling through the water at speeds greater than that of light in water.

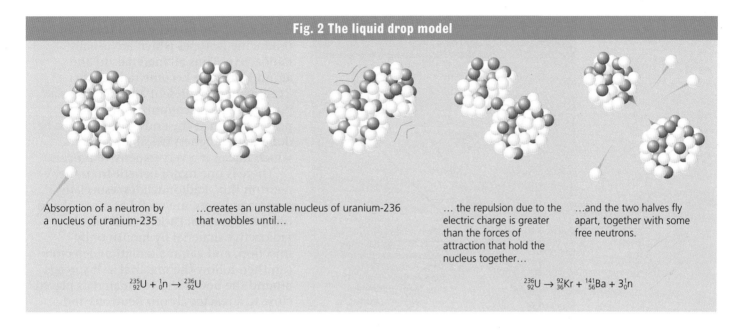

Fig. 2 The liquid drop model

Absorption of a neutron by a nucleus of uranium-235

...creates an unstable nucleus of uranium-236 that wobbles until...

... the repulsion due to the electric charge is greater than the forces of attraction that hold the nucleus together...

...and the two halves fly apart, together with some free neutrons.

$$^{235}_{92}U + ^{1}_{0}n \rightarrow ^{236}_{92}U$$

$$^{236}_{92}U \rightarrow ^{92}_{36}Kr + ^{141}_{56}Ba + 3^{1}_{0}n$$

the speed of light), predicts the amount of energy that is made available from a given mass loss.

Each nucleon in a nucleus has less mass than when they are free. The mass loss can be expressed in terms of **binding energy**. Any process that increases binding energy per nucleon (Fig. 3) reduces the total mass of the particles involved. (See Chapter 4 for more detail on mass difference and binding energies of nuclei.) There is thus a release of energy. Both **fission** (splitting) of heavy nuclei and **fusion** (joining) of light nuclei can result in energy release.

1 What parts do neutrons play in the fission of a single nucleus of uranium-235?

2 a How can both fission and fusion make energy available?
b Why would the fusion of two iron nuclei require an input of energy? Find out, or discuss, what this has to do with the death of stars.

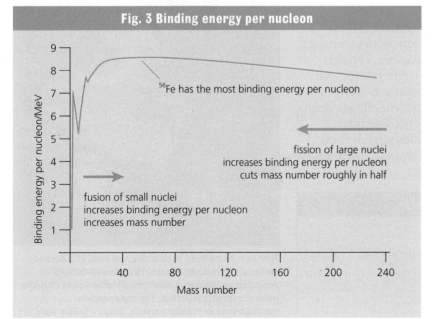

Fig. 3 Binding energy per nucleon

^{56}Fe has the most binding energy per nucleon

fission of large nuclei increases binding energy per nucleon cuts mass number roughly in half

fusion of small nuclei increases binding energy per nucleon increases mass number

Binding energy per nucleon/MeV

Mass number

Waste
Energy release is not the only consequence of fission. Nuclear power stations also produce radioactive waste. There are two main ways that waste is produced.

Daughter nuclei accumulate steadily as fission proceeds in a reactor. These nuclei have nearly the same ratio of neutrons to protons as their parent nucleus. That makes them neutron-rich compared with stable nuclides of their size (Fig. 4). This means the daughter nuclei are highly radioactive, usually have short half-lives and emit β^- radiation.

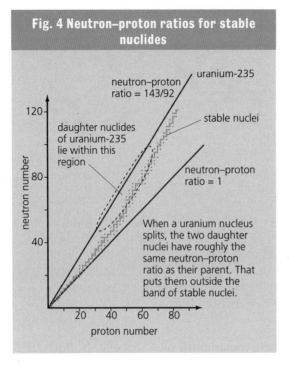

Fig. 4 Neutron–proton ratios for stable nuclides

uranium-235

neutron–proton ratio = 143/92

daughter nuclides of uranium-235 lie within this region

stable nuclei

neutron–proton ratio = 1

When a uranium nucleus splits, the two daughter nuclei have roughly the same neutron–proton ratio as their parent. That puts them outside the band of stable nuclei.

neutron number

proton number

numbers of the nuclei which they join, producing isotopes which are usually radioactive. Thus all materials in and around a reactor become radioactive. Eventually they present another disposal problem. The 'decommissioning' of a power station at the end of its life must be done to the highest possible standard, which makes it a very expensive process.

There is one major benefit from the neutron flux. Radionuclides, especially gamma emitters, are useful as medical and industrial tracers. Patients can take in radioactive material by mouth or by injection, and gamma radiation detectors can then follow the material as it spreads around the body. Selected materials placed close to a reactor absorb neutrons and provide a supply of tracer nuclides. For example:

$$^{23}_{11}Na + ^{1}_{0}n \rightarrow ^{24}_{11}Na$$

This highly radioactive material is classed as 'high level' waste (Table 1) and is kept cool to compensate for the continuous energy release from radioactive decay. Because many of the daughter nuclides have short half-lives, the activity of the waste eventually falls and heating is no longer a problem. But some of the nuclides do have long half-lives, and, even after it is cool enough to handle, the material must be isolated so that it cannot irradiate the environment.

Nuclear fission also creates waste in another way. Fission produces neutrons set free from the splitting nucleus. Though some neutrons remain in the reactor and play an active part in keeping it going, a continuous flow of neutrons emerges from the reactor in all directions. The reactor materials and surroundings absorb these neutrons. The neutrons change the mass

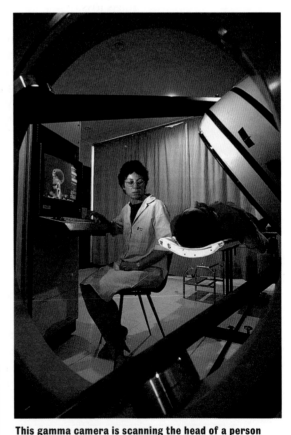

This gamma camera is scanning the head of a person suffering from bone cancer. The camera detects radiation emitted by a short-lived radionuclide that the patient recently ingested. The radionuclide concentrates in rapidly growing tissue – in this case the cancerous bone tissue.

Table 1 Grades of radioactive waste	
Type	**definition/radioactivity**
High level	separated fission products from irradiated fuels
Intermediate level	>12 GBq per tonne (β and γ)
	>4 GBq per tonne (α)
Low level	>400 KBq per tonne

This slab of glass contains all the high-level waste from a nuclear reaction that would supply a person with electricity for life.

Waste disposal

Neither the French nor any other nuclear industry has yet solved the problem of long term storage of nuclear waste. One plan is to embed this waste in glass, so that it cannot leak out, and bury it deep underground. In the meantime, the French nuclear industry separates high level nuclear waste from the fuel rods during fuel 'reprocessing' and stores it at a base on the Channel coast.

3 a Uranium-235 is radioactive. What radiation does it emit?
 b Explain fully how and why the radiation emitted from used nuclear fuel, removed from the reactor, is not the same as the radiation emitted by new fuel.

4 The concrete shielding around a reactor prevents significant escape of neutrons by absorbing them.
 a Concrete contains oxygen-16 chemically combined with other elements. Complete this nuclear reaction for an oxygen nucleus that absorbs a total of three neutrons.
 $^{16}_{8}O + 3\,^{1}_{0}n \rightarrow$
 b Show the nuclear reaction for the decay of the resulting oxygen nucleus. Use the Data section.
 c What might be the effect of such decays on the strength of the concrete?

Key ideas

- Medium-sized nuclei (such as iron and krypton) have a large binding energy per nucleon. Smaller and larger nuclei have less binding energy per nucleon.

- The energy released during fission is equal to the change in binding energy of the nucleons. The change in binding energy is accompanied by a change in mass, as predicted by Einstein ($E = mc^2$).

- Fission of a nucleus of uranium-235 can be triggered by the absorption of a neutron.

- The medium-sized daughter nuclei produced by fission are generally unstable with short half-lives.

- Neutrons from a reactor can produce artificial radionuclides. Many artificial nuclides are classed as hazardous high-level radioactive waste.

- Artificial radionuclides are used in medicine and industry as tracers and gamma emitters.

6.3 A controlled reaction

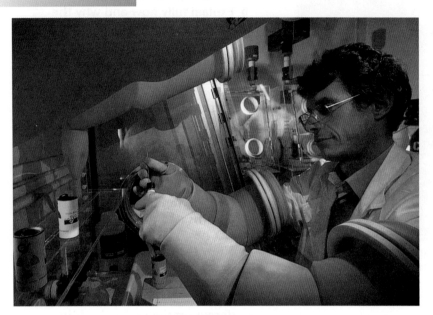

'As an engineer on the power plant I find it odd that people still imagine that a power station could become a nuclear bomb. This is not a real concern – it's a physical impossibilty.
There are other concerns and we bear in mind the need to control the process of generation tightly at every step when we design the plant.'

Fission bombs and fission reactors can both be made from uranium. Natural uranium, dug from rock, is more than 99% uranium-238. This does not split easily, though it does absorb neutrons. About 0.7% of the uranium is the fissioning isotope, uranium-235, that provides the source of energy in reactors.

The two isotopes are chemically identical and differ only in the masses of their nuclei. That makes it difficult and expensive to separate them. However, it can be done by taking advantage of the fact that in fluids, heavier atoms diffuse more slowly. Uranium that has an increased proportion of uranium-235 is called *enriched fuel*.

Fast and slow neutrons

In a bomb, a chain reaction (Fig. 5) runs wild throughout a ball of uranium. More than one of the neutrons speeding away from each fission induces fission in other nuclei. The fission rate, and rate of energy release, increases very rapidly for as long as the uranium lasts.

But the neutrons are fast – there is nothing to slow them down after they emerge from fissioning nuclei. In a ball of natural uranium nearly all of them would be absorbed by uranium-238. In this respect the behaviour of the two isotopes is exactly opposite – uranium-235 absorbs *slow* neutrons more easily than it absorbs fast ones, uranium-238 absorbs *fast* neutrons more easily than slow ones. Neutron speed is very important. To build a bomb the uranium must be heavily enriched. Otherwise, a chain reaction would not be possible.

To keep the chain reaction going inside a ball of enriched uranium, the ball must be above a certain mass, called the **critical mass**. A small ball would have a large surface compared to its volume. A high

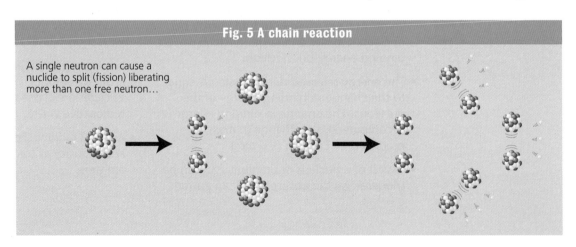

Fig. 5 A chain reaction

A single neutron can cause a nuclide to split (fission) liberating more than one free neutron...

Enriched uranium and a critical mass.

Q5 Two halves of a ball of uranium-235 initially contain 10^4 free neutrons.

a Estimate the number of neutrons that are freed after 1 μs if the two halves are brought together so that a rapidly growing chain reaction takes place.

b If each of these neutrons were to induce fission of a nucleus of uranium-235, what would be the energy release, i) in MeV, ii) in J?

The moderator and control rods

In a reactor, the chain reaction must not run wild but must keep going at a constant rate: an average of exactly one neutron from each fission event must induce fission in another uranium nucleus (Fig. 6). But a nuclear reactor *cannot* explode like a nuclear bomb.

A reactor contains a very high proportion of uranium-238 in its fuel, which absorbs fast neutrons but does not undergo fission. It *opposes* a chain reaction. Also, the uranium is spread throughout a large volume, much of the reactor being made of other materials. Critical mass can never be achieved. A chain reaction is only

proportion of the neutrons produced by fission would escape through the surface before being absorbed by uranium-235 and inducing new fission. To detonate a bomb, two pieces of uranium that are smaller than the critical mass are brought together, to make one large piece. The chain reaction then multiplies the number of freed neutrons in the uranium by a million million times in less than a microsecond.

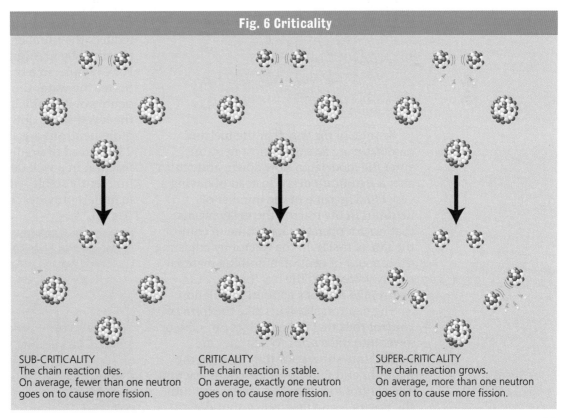

Fig. 6 Criticality

SUB-CRITICALITY
The chain reaction dies.
On average, fewer than one neutron goes on to cause more fission.

CRITICALITY
The chain reaction is stable.
On average, exactly one neutron goes on to cause more fission.

SUPER-CRITICALITY
The chain reaction grows.
On average, more than one neutron goes on to cause more fission.

made possible at all by making the reactor big enough to limit the proportion of neutrons that escape through its surface, and by *slowing down* the neutrons to much slower speeds than they have when they emerge from nuclei.

The neutrons are slowed by a **moderator** that surrounds the fuel rods. Neutrons speed out of the fuel rods and collide with the nuclei of the moderator, transferring some of their kinetic energy (Fig. 7). After several collisions, the neutrons return to the fuel. Their speeds are now comparable to that of particles their size in a hot gas – they are no longer fast neutrons but are called **thermal neutrons**.

Looking down at the top of a reactor. The yellow cylinders control the lowering and raising of the control rods.

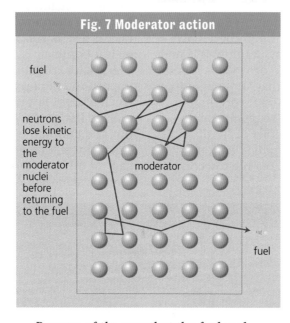

Fig. 7 Moderator action

fuel

neutrons lose kinetic energy to the moderator nuclei before returning to the fuel

moderator

fuel

Because of the way that the fuel and moderator are arranged, most neutrons enter the moderator, slow down, and return after a significant delay. Instead of having a very rapid increase in the number of neutrons in the reactor, the delay means that reactor operators have time to control the rate of fission in the reactor by adjusting the amount of neutron absorbing material that is slotted into the reactor. They can control the reactor's neutron population.

The neutron absorbers take the form of **control rods** that the operators can raise or lower into the reactor. When they are pushed into the reactor they mop up the neutrons and slow down the chain reaction. The control rods can drop all the way into the reactor for an emergency shut-down.

Negative feedback

Control rods are not the only defence against the chain reaction getting out of hand. If the rate of fission increases, then so does the temperature of the fuel and of the moderator. An increase in temperature reduces the number of neutrons that can be absorbed by uranium-235 and cause fission. For example, in a water-cooled reactor, the hotter the water the more it mops up neutrons. Also the hotter the moderator the less it slows down the neutrons, and so more neutrons are absorbed by uranium-238 instead of uranium-235. A chain reaction in a well designed reactor is inherently stable – the behaviour of the materials provides some negative feedback (Fig. 8).

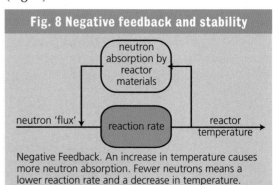

Fig. 8 Negative feedback and stability

neutron absorption by reactor materials

neutron 'flux'

reaction rate

reactor temperature

Negative Feedback. An increase in temperature causes more neutron absorption. Fewer neutrons means a lower reaction rate and a decrease in temperature.

Out of control?

The Chernobyl disaster of 1986 spread nuclear waste isotopes – fission products – over a huge area. In countries far from the exploded reactor, such as France and the UK, thousands of people have yet to die of cancer as a result of food and drink contaminated by Chernobyl's dust. This was one of the world's worst industrial accidents.

Chernobyl was not a nuclear explosion. Because of the design of the reactor and unauthorised experiments by the operating staff, the chain reaction did speed up and cause the reactor temperature to rise very quickly. It was boiling water that burst the reactor open. The hydrogen released from the water then exploded. It was an ordinary physical and chemical reaction, but the resulting fire sent a great deal of radioactive material up into the atmosphere. If the power plant had been designed with proper containment, the misery that followed would never have happened.

6 a What are thermal neutrons?
b What is the difference in behaviour of uranium-235 nuclei towards thermal and fast neutrons?

Key ideas

- Common uranium-238 absorbs fast neutrons easily – opposing a chain reaction

- Nuclear bombs use highly enriched uranium (mostly uranium-235) in a critical mass to sustain a chain reaction.

- A controlled reaction, involving fission of uranium-235, can be sustained in a reactor using a moderator. Moderators slow the neutrons down.

- Control rods are used to absorb neutrons. They control the reaction rate.

- Control rods can quickly stop the reaction in an emergency shutdown.

6.4 Policy decisions, design decisions

Containment

Containment is not just a problem in the nuclear industry. The worst industrial accident in the world occurred two years before Chernobyl at Bhopal in India. A huge cloud of toxic methyl-icocyanate gas was released from the plant because it had

The slums near the Union Carbide plant in Bhopal.

Practising in a model of the reactor at the Three Mile Island nuclear installation. An accident in 1979 flooded the real building with hazardous radioactive material. Secondary containment ensured that the incident was not a full-scale environmental disaster.

inadequate containment built into the design of the factory. It immediately killed 4000 people. Hundreds of thousands of people in the neighbouring towns were affected by physiological and genetic disorders.

The danger of releasing radioactive material into the environment means that containment for a nuclear power station is a primary concern. The Chernobyl nuclear power station was built to a design known as RBMK, a design unique to the old Soviet Union. The RBMK reactor only had what is called 'primary' containment – the reactor building itself – which had to contain all possible releases of radioactivity. All other

designs of power station ever built have 'secondary' containment, an extra layer of containment built around the power station. Effective secondary containment costs, but it is a cost that has to be paid.

Choosing a coolant

In a coal or gas fired system, the pipes that carry the steam to the turbine come into close contact with the burning fuel. But in a nuclear power station there are two systems of pipes. The *primary system* transfers energy from the hot heart of the reactor where the nuclear processes are taking place. Then in a heat exchanger or steam generator the pipes of the primary system run close to pipes of a *secondary system* which carries the steam for turning the turbines (Fig. 9).

The reason for this double system is that coolant material near the fuel rods absorbs neutrons, so some of its nuclei become neutron-rich and radioactive. Such material must not be allowed to escape and is kept sealed within the primary cooling system. The steam that turns the turbines cannot be kept from contact with the atmosphere so easily. It flows in the secondary cooling system that has no direct contact with the reactor.

The coolant must, of course, be fluid: gas or liquid. A high **specific heat capacity** is desirable. Materials with high specific heat capacities can carry energy away very effectively without need for very high temperatures. A material with a low specific heat capacity can still be used provided that it flows quickly around the system, transferring energy quickly enough to match the rate of energy release by the chain reaction in the reactor.

The first French nuclear power stations were gas-cooled, using carbon dioxide (Fig. 9). Carbon dioxide is chemically inert and does not react with pipework. As a gas it can be pressurised and it can flow quickly around the pipes from reactor to steam generator. Another advantage is that neither carbon nor oxygen nuclei are strong absorbers of neutrons and therefore the gas does not become highly radioactive. It can be allowed to pass out of the reactor's concrete shielding to the steam generator.

Fig. 9 Gas cooled reactors

control rods
primary cooling system
secondary cooling system
concrete shielding
high pressure steam to turbine
water in from turbine
fuel rods
graphite moderator   steel pressure vessel   coolant flow (carbon dioxide)

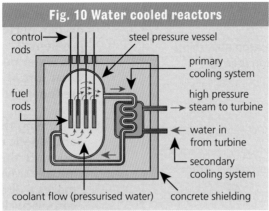

Fig. 10 Water cooled reactors

control rods → steel pressure vessel

fuel rods → primary cooling system

→ high pressure steam to turbine

← water in from turbine

secondary cooling system

coolant flow (pressurised water) — concrete shielding

7 Explain why the steam generator in a PWR must be inside the reactor shielding, whereas in a gas-cooled reactor it can be on the outside.

8 Describe one advantage and one disadvantage of water over carbon dioxide as reactor coolant.

The Americans, however, developed smaller, water-cooled, systems for use in military submarines (Fig. 10). Water has a particularly high specific heat capacity. These reactors do not require a large block of graphite as a moderator because the coolant water itself has a moderating effect. They can therefore be quite small, and cheaper to build.

One disadvantage is that the hydrogen nuclei in the water are comparatively good neutron absorbers and become radioactive, so the water must always be kept inside the concrete shielding. Also, natural uranium is not suitable as a fuel for pressurised water reactors. The neutrons are not slowed enough by the water to maintain a chain reaction when the proportion of uranium-235 in the fuel is too small. The uranium must be enriched. French nuclear power stations built since the 1970s have been American-style pressurised-water reactors, or PWRs.

Nuclear submarines use the much more compact water-cooled reactors.

Choosing moderator materials
The free neutrons produced by fission in the fuel rods are very energetic and not easily absorbed by nuclei of uranium-235. The moderator is there to slow the neutrons down so that they return into the fuel rods at thermal speeds and induce more fission to maintain a stable chain reaction.

A moderator should not have a high tendency to absorb neutrons. Once neutrons are absorbed, they cannot induce further fission and cannot contribute to the chain reaction. Also, the moderator would then become more radioactive. For example, 'heavy water', in which the hydrogen is a heavy isotope (hydrogen-2, also known as deuterium), is a better moderator than ordinary water. The heavier isotope of hydrogen is already neutron rich and so has a low tendency to absorb more neutrons.

Water, heavy or not, contains nuclei which are quite small. When two objects collide the energy is more evenly shared if the particles have similar size. Neutrons colliding with large nuclei would lose only a small proportion of their energy on each collision – they would be inclined to bounce off with little change in their speed.

Gas cooled reactors use graphite (carbon) as the moderator. This, like heavy water, has the necessary low tendency to absorb neutrons, together with quite small particle size.

Choosing control rod material
Control rods that can be inserted and removed from a reactor make it possible for power station staff to control the fission

Table 2 Neutron absorption	
Nuclide	Thermal neutron absorbing cross section (barns)
$^{1}_{1}H$	3.32×10^{-1}
$^{2}_{1}H$	5.30×10^{-4}
$^{12}_{6}C$	3.40×10^{-3}
$^{16}_{8}O$	2.70×10^{-4}
$^{238}_{92}U$	7.59
$^{10}_{5}B$	7.59×10^{2}
$^{114}_{48}Cd$	2.45×10^{3}
1 barn = 10^{-28} m^2	

rate. Control rods are made of materials that are good at absorbing neutrons (Table 2).

Deciding on a standard reactor design

Development costs for a large project such as a nuclear power station are very high. These will be even higher if designs have to be worked out each time from basic principles. So the French developed three standard designs for 900 MW, 1300 MW and 1450 MW reactors. Any one of these designs can be built in five years or less. It is the low investment costs that have made French electricity as cheap as it is.

PWRs use water as their moderator as well as their coolant.

a If ordinary water is installed in a new reactor what will happen to the hydrogen nuclei under the influence of a constant stream of neutrons?

b Use data from Table 2 to consider whether absorption of neutrons by oxygen nuclei in the water is a problem.

c The water becomes radioactive. What sort of radiation does it then predominantly emit?

10 a Assuming that both momentum and kinetic energy are conserved, calculate the speed of a neutron initially travelling at 10^5 m s^{-1} that makes a direct hit on a stationary carbon nucleus in a reactor moderator block.

b If the temperature of a moderator is 800 K, use the kinetic theory equation, $\frac{1}{2}m\overline{c^2} = \frac{3}{2}kT$, to calculate the speed of a thermal neutron within the moderator.

11 a Compare the required neutron absorbing properties of coolant, moderator and control rod materials.

b Use the table to select two possible control rod materials.

12 a Calculate the minimum rate at which fuel rods must decrease in mass in a power unit with a 900 MW power output.

b Why will actual rate of mass loss be bigger than this?

Key ideas

- Containment is crucial to the safe running of a nuclear power plant.

- The coolant in a reactor must carry away the thermal energy to prevent overheating.

- Moderators need to be able to absorb the energy of fast neutrons, slowing the neutrons down so that they have a greater chance of inducing fission.

- Control rods need to be able to absorb neutrons, so that the chain reaction can be controlled.

6.5 Too many answers

The French nuclear industry claims to be safe and clean – it produces no acid rain, unlike fossil-fuel power stations. As nuclear electricity generation is not based on a chemical burning process, there is no direct production of carbon dioxide, which is the main cause of global climate change. Nuclear power stations do not require rivers to be blocked, valleys to be flooded, or large areas of land set aside for noisy and unsightly aerogenerators.

On the other hand, the problem of waste disposal has not been satisfactorily solved and there have been a number of significant nuclear accidents that have released radioactive material into the environment. Digging for uranium ore is also very hazardous to miners, especially where dust and radioactive gas can accumulate. Nuclear reactors can also provide the raw materials for building bombs.

The debate expands to take in all manner of concerns, far from the specialism of the nuclear scientist, with a variety of answers for each question raised.

Necessity is the mother of invention

The scientists and engineers have been highly inventive in solving the problems that building nuclear power stations has thrown at them. Solving those problems was seen as an economic necessity at a time when the demand for energy was getting ever larger. The economic situation, however, has changed.

We are now becoming more conscious of energy consumption. This and the development of new technologies that consume less power has led to a slowing down of the demand for electricity. The 1990s have seen very few nuclear power stations being built. It could be that in the years to come, the simple mathematics of economics could make the technology of nuclear power redundant – a solution with no problem to solve.

Q 13 Imagine that, following an accident in a nuclear power station, 1 kg of partly used fuel from a reactor, still mostly uranium but with significant amounts of daughter nuclides, is spread evenly over an area of 1000 km by 1000 km.

a 1 kg = 6.0×10^{26} u (atomic mass units). If the average mass of each nuclei in the escaped material is 222 u, how many nuclei are in the kg of material?

b How many nuclei are spread onto each m^2?

c The uranium in the escaped material has a long half-life and contributes little to the radioactivity of the sample. Suppose that 0.1% of the sample is made up of daughter nuclides with an average half-life of 100 hours. Estimate the activity, in Bq, of:
i) the whole of the escaped material;
ii) the material found in one square metre;
iii) the material found in 5 square centimetres (approximately the area of a GM tube window).

d The background count recorded by a GM tube is normally in the region of 20 Bq. Would you recommend drinking the milk from a cow that had been grazing within this 1000 km by 1000 km area?

e Use the scale on the map on page 57 to estimate how this area compares with the land area of France.

Cambridge at the dawn of the electronic era, when gas lamps lined the streets.

British Telecom Network Management Centre.

At the British Telecom Network Management Centre in Shropshire, engineers work at their computer terminals and keep an eye on the latest television news from around the world. Their computers direct international telephone calls around the most efficient routes. All of the equipment depends upon electron technology. Effective communication was quite a different story in the era before the discovery of the electron.

It was only in the middle of the nineteenth century that the electric telegraph was developed. This (then) new and miraculously fast means of communication allowed coded messages to be 'tapped out' along the wires and received almost instantly. Nobody understood the processes going on inside the wires, but the technology worked. Large laboratories devoted to the development of telegraph and electrification networks were built.

Towards the end of the century, an academic working in one of those quiet laboratories in a back street of Cambridge, discovered the electron. It was soon realised that it was the effect of forces between electrons that carried the telegraph messages. Since then there has been an explosion of industries founded on electron based technology – a new industrial revolution. A revolution in the way we live from day to day.

This telegraph machine, invented in 1855 by a professor of music, could send 30 words a minute.

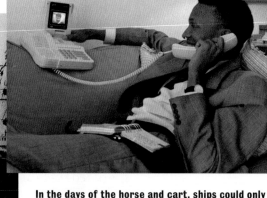

In the days of the horse and cart, ships could only communicate with each other by waving flags, and flickering flames were all that there was to watch on a winter's evening.

7.1 Learning objectives

After working through this chapter, you should be able to:

- **describe** the equipment with which electrons were discovered;

- **explain** the process of thermionic emission;

- **explain** the motion of an electron in a uniform electric field;

- **explain** the motion of an electron in a uniform magnetic field;

- **describe** a method of measuring the specific charge (e/m) of electrons;

- **describe** the motion of a charged drop falling at terminal velocity in terms of viscous drag;

- **explain** how measurements on a charged oil droplet moving in an electric field can provide a measurement of the charge on an electron.

7.2 One technology leads to another

Michael Faraday demonstrated the link between electrical behaviour and magnetic behaviour in the 1830s. His work made it possible to build motors and generators, and to make electrically driven vacuum pumps. Such devices made it possible to achieve very low pressures inside sealed glass containers, and to apply high voltages to metal electrodes fixed inside glass flasks and tubes. People experimented with gases kept at very low pressures inside the glass containers. They watched the coloured glow from different gases, and analysed the spectra. They noticed that at a high enough voltage even the glass itself would glow.

Cathode rays, curiosity and controversy
Cathode rays, which came from a metal plate inside a glass tube and made the glass glow, were discovered in the 1850s. There were conflicting ideas about what the cathode rays were. In the late nineteenth century, scientists suspected that space was filled by a massless entity which they called the **aether** (pronounced 'ether'). Cathode rays were thought, by some, to be waves in this aether. Thomson supposed that cathode rays were particles and devised experiments to test the idea.

Electrical lighting did not become a practical reality until many years after Faraday's experiments. The problem was that the thin filaments oxidised rapidly in air. When it became possible to evacuate glass 'bulbs' the problem was solved. The same vacuum technology led to the discovery of electrons.

CATHODE RAYS.

By J.J.THOMSON, M.A., F.R.S.,
Cavendish Professor of Experimental Physics, Cambridge.

THE EXPERIMENTS discussed in this paper were undertaken in the hope of gaining some information as to the nature of cathode rays ... According to the almost unanimous opinion of German physicists they are due to some process in the aether ... another view of these rays is that ... they are in fact wholly material, and that they mark the paths of particles of matter charged with negative electricity ... The following experiments were carried out to test some of the consequences of the electrified-particle theory.

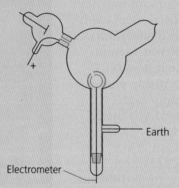

Earth

Electrometer

Two coaxial cylinders with slits in them are placed in a bulb connected with a discharge tube; the cathode rays ... do not fall upon the cylinders unless they are deflected by a magnet. The outer cylinder is connected with the Earth, the inner with the electrometer. When the cathode rays (whose path was traced by the phosphorescence on the glass) did not fall on the slit, the electrical charge sent to the electrometer ... was small and irregular; when, however, the rays were bent by a magnet so as to fall on the slit there was a large charge of negative electricity sent to the electrometer. I was surprised at the magnitude of the charge

... Thus this experiment shows that however we twist and deflect the cathode rays by magnetic forces, the negative electrification follows the same path as the rays, and that this negative electrification is indissolubly connected with the cathode rays.

[Thomson goes on to discuss the effect of an electric field on cathode rays ...]

Deflexion of the Cathode Rays by an Electrostatic Field

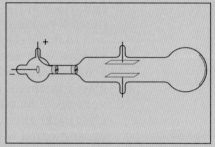

At high exhaustions [a strong vacuum, or low pressure] the rays were deflected when the two aluminium plates were connected with the terminals of a battery of small storage-cells; the rays were depressed when the upper plate was connected with the negative pole of the battery, the lower with the positive, and raised when the upper plate was connected with the positive, the lower with the negative pole. The deflexion was proportional to the difference of potential between the plates, and I could detect the deflexion when the potential difference was as small as two volts. It was only when the vacuum was a good one that the deflexion took place.

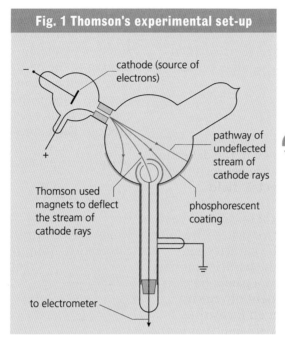

Fig. 1 Thomson's experimental set-up

- cathode (source of electrons)
- pathway of undeflected stream of cathode rays
- Thomson used magnets to deflect the stream of cathode rays
- phosphorescent coating
- to electrometer
- +
- −

An Irish physicist, Johnstone Stoney, had already suggested that the processes of electrolysis could be neatly explained by the existence of charge carrying particles, which he called electrons. Thomson acknowledged the idea by using the same name for his 'material' cathode rays.

1 **What 'new' (nineteenth century) technologies did Thomson use in his experiments?**

2 **Summarise the evidence that Thomson used to support his idea that cathode rays were made of small, negatively charged particles.**

Key ideas

- Cathode rays can be deflected by an electrical field or a magnetic field.
- Cathode rays are negatively charged particles called electrons.

7.3 Thomson's balancing act

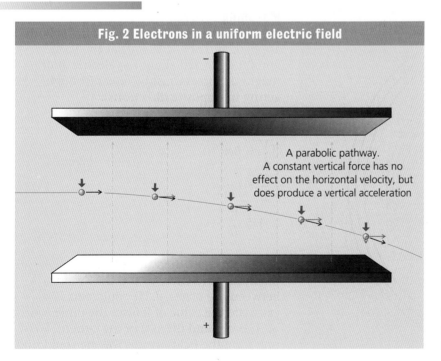

Fig. 2 Electrons in a uniform electric field

A parabolic pathway. A constant vertical force has no effect on the horizontal velocity, but does produce a vertical acceleration

−

+

Thomson was working to a hypothesis: that cathode rays might be beams of particles. Which meant they must have a certain mass and a certain charge. He designed a new experiment to determine what they were.

Thomson made a tube in which he could apply electric *and* magnetic fields at the same time. Two metal plates provided an electric field. (Electric fields accelerate electrons along a parabolic path, see Fig. 2.) The magnetic field came from coils carrying a large current. These provided a strong uniform magnetic field with evenly spaced parallel field-lines. (Magnetic fields like this force electrons to move in a circular path, see Fig. 3.)

Thomson built his apparatus so that the two fields produced deflection in opposite directions. Thomson then adjusted the strengths of the fields until there was zero net deflection – the effects of the two fields balanced or cancelled out.

If the cathode rays had charge e, then the force, F_E, on an electron due to the electric field would be:

$$F_E = \frac{eV}{d}$$

where V is the p.d. applied to the deflecting plates, and d is the distance between them. V/d is also called the **electric field strength**.

Note that the electrical force always acts perpendicularly to the two plates. The force is also constant while the particles are between the plates. So the particles moving in an electric field follow a parabolic path – with a constant component of velocity parallel to the plates but an increasing component of velocity perpendicular to the plates.

The force on an electron due to the magnetic field is given by:

$$F_B = Bev$$

where B is the magnetic field strength (flux density) and v is the velocity of the particles.

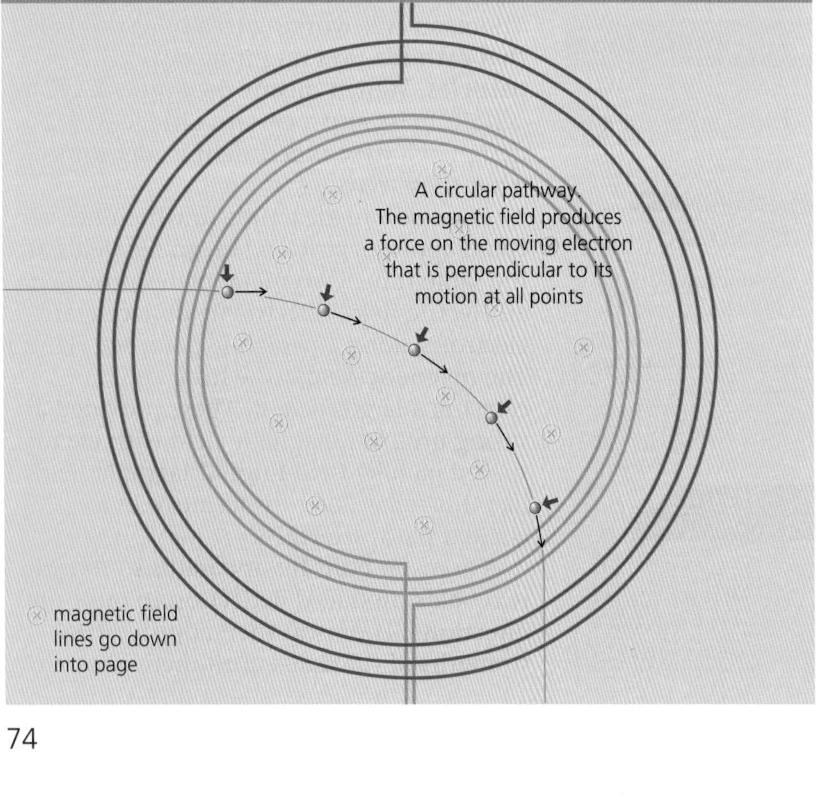

Unlike the force from the electric field, the magnetic force does not always act along the same direction, but turns as the motion of the particles turns. The force is always perpendicular to the motion of the electron. That is the characteristic of a centripetal force, which results in circular motion. The radius of the circle that the electrons move in is determined by the size of the centripetal force:

$$F_{centripetal} = \frac{mv^2}{r}$$

When the centripetal force is entirely due to the force from the magnetic field:

$$F_B = F_{centripetal}$$
$$Bev = \frac{mv^2}{r}$$

Rearranging this expression we can deduce that the electrons move in a path of radius:

$$r = \frac{mv}{Be}$$

and at a speed:

$$v = \frac{Ber}{m}$$

Matching forces

With the electric and magnetic fields both applied, and adjusted so that the particles are not deflected at all, the electric and magnetic forces must be equal (though acting in opposite directions):

$$F_E = F_B$$
$$\frac{eV}{d} = Bev$$
$$\frac{V}{d} = Bv$$
$$v = \frac{V}{dB}$$

Thomson knew the value of the applied potential difference, V, and the distance between the plates, d. He could also calculate the value of B from the dimensions of the coils and the size of the current. So by opposing the fields in this way he could find out the speed of the electrons.

Fig. 3 Electrons in a uniform magnetic field

A circular pathway. The magnetic field produces a force on the moving electron that is perpendicular to its motion at all points

⊗ magnetic field lines go down into page

He already knew that the velocity of the electrons is given by $v = Bre/m$ so:

$$v = \frac{V}{dB} = \frac{Bre}{m}$$

which gives $\dfrac{e}{m} = \dfrac{V}{dB^2r}$

The quantity e/m, the **specific charge** of the electron, was important to Thomson, and other physicists of the time, because it was amazingly high. The value for e/m for electrons is 1.7×10^{11} C kg^{-1}. This is 1836 times bigger than the specific charge for protons. Electrons have a lot of charge crammed in to a small mass.

The constancy of e/m for electrons from a variety of sources and different elements signalled that the electron was a **fundamental particle**.

3 What is the specific charge of:
  a a proton?
  b an alpha particle?
  c a neutron?
  d a nucleus of gold-197 (atomic number 79)?

4 Work out the magnetic field strength required to produce zero deflection of an electron beam when combined with an electric field of strength 10^4 Vm^{-1} (i.e. $V/d = 10^4$ V m^{-1}), and which when applied on its own produces circular motion with radius 10 cm.

Key ideas

- An electrical field has a field strength determined by the potential applied, V, and the separation, d. Field strength $E = V/d$.

- An electrical field exerts a force on a particle with charge q:

$$F_E = \frac{qV}{d}$$

- A magnetic field, of field strength B, exerts a force on a particle with charge q moving at velocity v:

$$F_B = Bqv$$

The force is always at a right angle to the direction of motion.

- Thomson was able to calculate e/m by balancing the electrical and magnetic force on a beam of electrons.

- The specific charge (value of e/m) for an electron is nearly 2000 times larger than that of a hydrogen ion (proton).

7.4 The value of e

Once the value of e/m had been identified, physicists attempted to evaluate the value of e itself. An experiment was devised by Robert Millikan. The apparatus he used was remarkably simple (many schools and colleges still have a set), but the experimental technique was incredibly delicate and took a lot of patience.

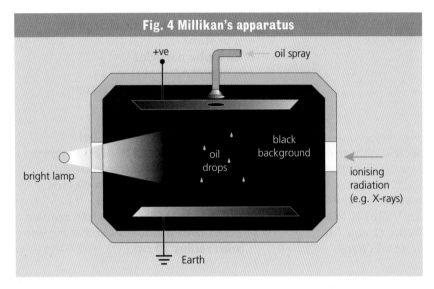

Fig. 4 Millikan's apparatus

+ve
oil spray
bright lamp
oil drops
black background
ionising radiation (e.g. X-rays)
Earth

Millikan used a pair of metal plates mounted horizontally, with a hole in the upper plate. The plates were sealed in a chamber to keep the main part of the apparatus free from dust and air currents (Fig. 4).

Millikan sprayed fine oil droplets into the space above the upper plate, and a small number of droplets found their way through the hole into the space between the plates. Against a black background, Millikan could see the tiny droplets as they scattered light from a bright lamp at the side of the apparatus. He wrote that this arrangement made a droplet look like 'a brilliant star on a black background.'

Because of their small size, oil droplets quickly reach their **terminal velocity**. Terminal velocity is reached by a falling object when its weight is balanced by an upwards force. Zero net force results in zero acceleration and a constant velocity (Fig. 5). Millikan measured the velocity of the oil drops by timing a fall between two set levels.

The force balancing the oil droplets is largely due to the **viscous force**, or drag, caused by the oil drop pushing its way through the air (air buoyancy, or upthrust, is a much less important factor). Viscous force can be calculated from an equation that is often called **Stokes' law**:

$$F_{viscous} = 6\pi\eta rv$$

where v is the drop's velocity, r is the drop's radius and η is known as the coefficient of viscosity of air ($\eta = 1.8 \times 10^{-5}$ N s m^{-2}).

The radius of the oil drops used in Millikan's experiment are too small to measure directly. You can find a drop's size indirectly by measuring its terminal velocity. Then you equate the weight of the drop with the viscous drag of the air:

$$mg = 6\pi\eta rv.$$

If you assume the oil drop is a tiny sphere, then the mass of the oil drop is given by density times its spherical volume:

$$m = \rho V$$
$$= \rho \tfrac{4}{3}\pi r^3$$
$$\text{so, } \left(\rho \tfrac{4}{3}\pi r^3\right)g = 6\pi\eta rv$$

This can be rearranged to give:

$$r^2 = \frac{6\pi\eta v}{\rho \tfrac{4}{3}\pi g}$$
$$r = \sqrt{\frac{9\eta v}{2\rho g}}$$

So you can calculate r from known constants (η, ρ and g) and the drop's terminal velocity (v). The radius (or mass) of a drop is crucial to the next part of the experiment.

Introducing the electrical force

Millikan used an electric field to stop the falling oil drops. The applied potential difference forced a few drops to fall faster

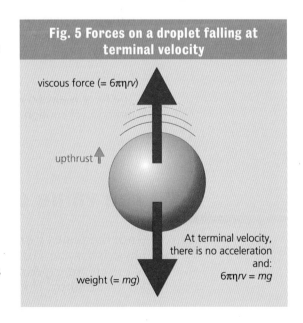

Fig. 5 Forces on a droplet falling at terminal velocity

viscous force ($= 6\pi\eta rv$)

upthrust

weight ($= mg$)

At terminal velocity, there is no acceleration and:
$6\pi\eta rv = mg$

than before, but some became stationary or began to move upwards, quickly reaching a new terminal velocity. The oil drops that had acquired an electrical charge were experiencing the electrical force.

Millikan noticed that oil droplets would occasionally make a *sudden* transition from one steady upwards speed to another, sometimes slowing down and sometimes speeding up. The oil drops were not gaining or losing their charge continuously, but in jumps. Millikan realised that this observation supported the idea that 'all electric charges, however produced, are exact multiples of one definite, elementary, electrical charge … electrical charge [consists] of an exact number of specks, or atoms of electricity.'

 5 **In what way is Millikan's use of the word 'atom' different from present day use?**

Millikan attempted to calculate the magnitude of his 'one definite, elementary, electrical charge'. This is done most simply by adjusting the electrical field to hold an oil drop steady. Then the downwards weight of the oil drop is matched by the upwards electrical force, and since the droplet is stationary there is no viscous force (Fig. 6).

Electric force on a charge is given by charge multiplied by electric field strength.

Fig. 6 Forces on a stationary oil drop

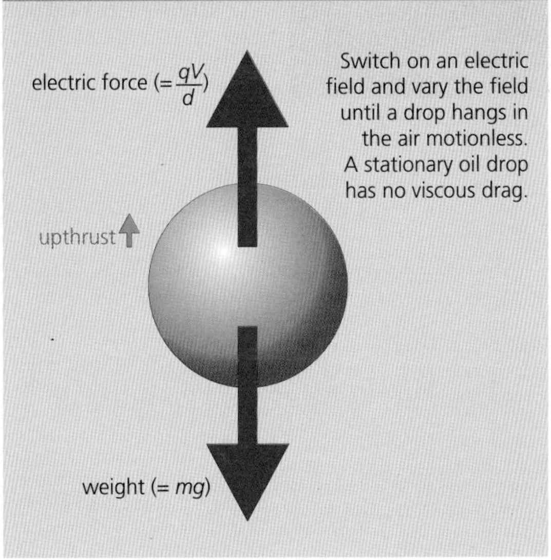

electric force ($= \frac{qV}{d}$)

upthrust

Switch on an electric field and vary the field until a drop hangs in the air motionless. A stationary oil drop has no viscous drag.

weight ($= mg$)

Recall that field strength is potential difference divided by distance.

$$F_{\text{electrical}} = \text{charge} \times \text{field strength}$$
$$= q \times \frac{V}{d}$$

This electrical force is balanced by the weight (force) due to gravity. (Notice that the force due to a gravitational field is expressed in a similar manner to the force due to the electric field. Instead of charge times *electric* field strength, weight is given as mass times *gravitational* field strength.) The gravitational field strength of the Earth at its surface is g:

$$F_{\text{gravity}} = \text{mass} \times \text{field strength}$$
$$= m \times g$$

Again, assuming that the drop is a sphere of density ρ, the mass is:

$$m = \text{density} \times \text{volume}$$
$$= \rho \times \tfrac{4}{3}\pi r^3$$

Now we can equate the electrical and gravitational forces on a static drop:

$$F_{\text{gravity}} = F_{\text{electrical}}$$
$$\rho \tfrac{4}{3}\pi r^3 g = \frac{qV}{d}$$

which can be rearranged to give:

$$q = \frac{4\rho\pi r^3 g d}{3V}$$

We have already seen how r can be calculated for these tiny drops. Millikan could easily measure ρ (the density of the oil used), V and d, and he knew the value of the constant g (9.8 N kg^{-1}). So using this procedure, and after *much* calculation, he derived the charge on a drop. The experiment is improved by using ionising radiation to dislodge some of the drop's charge and then recalculating the new charge based on the new potential difference needed to hold the drop stationary.

The results from Millikan's experiments conclusively proved that any change in electric charge on a drop was always a multiple of the same value. This value, 1.6×10^{-19} C, is the fundamental quantity of charge carried by every electron and every proton (though opposite in value) in the Universe.

Key ideas

- The terminal velocity of a small droplet is determined by the viscous drag of the air. The viscous drag can be calculated by Stokes' law:

  $F_{viscous} = 6\pi\eta r v.$

- The mass, or radius, of a small drop can be calculated using Stokes' law and the drop's density and terminal velocity.

- Millikan's experiment to calculate the magnitude of the charge on an electron worked by balancing the weight of an oil drop with the electrical force on it.

- Millikan showed that charge is always a multiple of a certain value. This demonstrates the quantisation of charge.

7.5 Conclusion

Lighting, radio, TV and computers all began with knowledge of the behaviour of electrons in vacuums. The knowledge was developed in a Cambridge laboratory, with a scientist using the latest techniques to explore the fundamental nature of matter. Neither Thomson nor Millikan were trying to become rich. They were not trying to provide the beginnings of new global industries. Nobody imagined that their knowledge would lead to vast networks of almost immediate communication, or entertainment that would change people's lives all around the world. They were just trying to find out more.

Seen in a different light

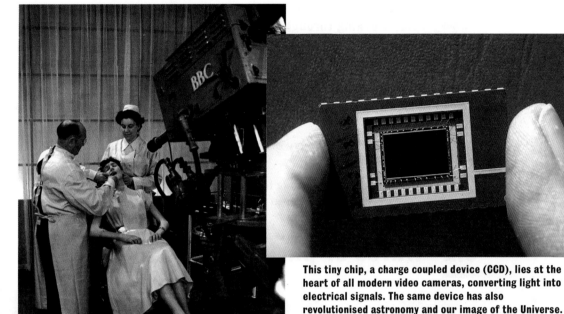

Images of a bygone age. Bulky television cameras were difficult to move around and limited what you could do and show on television. Changing technology means that you can now hold a camera in the palm of your hand.

This tiny chip, a charge coupled device (CCD), lies at the heart of all modern video cameras, converting light into electrical signals. The same device has also revolutionised astronomy and our image of the Universe. The technology works because light acts like a wave and a particle.

Living things can sense their surroundings by sight, sound or traces of chemicals. A human brain sits in a dark bony shell, and it knows about the world largely through the sense of sight. Light is important to us, and it is not surprising that scientists have given a lot of attention to ideas about light.

A lot of our technology is based around images and light. From early camera obscuras to digital photography and the latest most sensitive deep-space telescopes, this technology has developed hand in hand with our understanding of light as a physical phenomenon. The theories of light have seen a variety of surprising developments. The most revolutionary of changes in 20th century physics – quantum mechanics and relativity – are both due to developments in the theory of light.

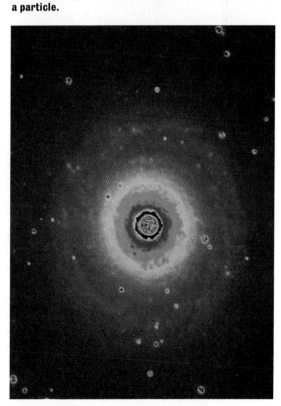

CCDs can detect single photons of light. This image would just appear as a bright spot on ordinary camera film, but the sensitive CCD detector reveals the delicate spiral arms of a galaxy.

After working through this chapter, you should be able to:

- **compare** competing 18th century ideas about light;

- **explain** the significance of diffraction and interference of light to accepted scientific theory;

- **describe** the discovery of invisible radiations related to light;

- **recall** Maxwell's formula for the speed of electromagnetic waves in a vacuum;

- **explain** how wave theory failed to describe the characteristics of black-body radiation;

- **explain** how and why the theory of 'quantised' energy developed;

- **understand** the significance of Einstein's explanation of the photoelectric effect.

8.2 Waves or particles?

The geometry of light explained the principles of the popular and fashionable camera obscura.

A camera obscura produces remarkably vivid images of the world outside. Although it is just a large pinhole camera, the quality of the moving image is surprising if you are only used to the graininess of television.

Light in the 'Dark Ages'

Some ancient thinkers (including the famous philosopher Aristotle) imagined that we see by sending something out from our eyes, rather like the way that bats send out bursts of sound. In the so-called 'Dark Ages', when science was very much alive and developing vigorously in the Arab world, Arab mathematicians used the idea of 'rays' of light – pathways spreading in straight lines from a source of light. The idea allowed Al-Haytham (965–1040) to work out the geometry of vision, and to describe reflection, refraction and the workings of the camera obscura.

Johannes Kepler (1571–1630) wrote a book (the *Paralipomena* published in 1604) that summarised and updated geometrical optics based on the renewed interest in, and practise of, realistic painting. The geometry fitted with observations, such as the fact that near objects appear to be bigger than far objects. It helped artists to draw and paint using 'perspective' to give an impression of real depth on a flat surface.

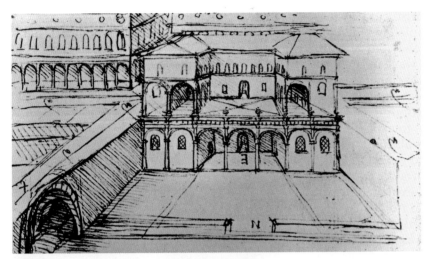

This sketch from the notebooks of the great painter Leonardo da Vinci shows that he made use of geometry to help him get perspective right.

Theories of light

The lenses of a telescope separate one colour of light from another, so that a star can appear bluish or reddish, depending on the adjustment of the telescope. This effect is called **chromatic aberration** (Fig. 1), and it is an irritation to astronomers.

Isaac Newton (1642–1727) tried to develop lenses that got rid of this chromatic aberration, but he failed. In the process he discovered that white light is an even mixture of all colours. A prism and a stream of white light were all that was needed to demonstrate the splitting, or 'dispersion', of light into colours. People found Newton's idea that colours are components of white light to be convincing. So when he went on to create explanations of the behaviour of light in terms of assorted *particles*, people were inclined to be convinced again.

A prism, Newton said, exerts different forces on different particles of light, and separates them. Refraction, he said, happened when the particles changed speed, speeding up, for example, when they pass from air into glass or water (Fig. 2).

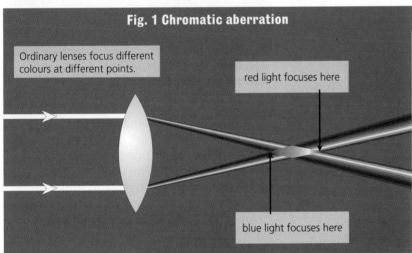

Fig. 1 Chromatic aberration

Ordinary lenses focus different colours at different points.

red light focuses here

blue light focuses here

Dispersion by a prism.

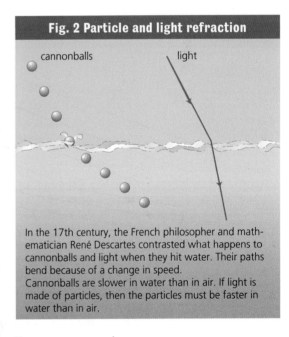

Fig. 2 Particle and light refraction

cannonballs

light

In the 17th century, the French philosopher and mathematician René Descartes contrasted what happens to cannonballs and light when they hit water. Their paths bend because of a change in speed.
Cannonballs are slower in water than in air. If light is made of particles, then the particles must be faster in water than in air.

1 a Suppose that light is made of particles. Draw a diagram to show how a beam of particles refracts if, upon moving into water, they decelerate in the direction of the normal. Draw another diagram to show refraction if the particles accelerate in the direction of the normal.
   b Explain how your diagrams contrast with your understanding of how the refraction of light works.

A Dutch scientist, Christiaan Huygens (1629–1695), had a completely different way of explaining the behaviour of light. He thought of light as a wave in the form of a series of irregular movements, and he used this to provide a neat explanation of refraction (Fig. 3). A major difference with Newton's ideas was that, to explain refraction, Huygens' impulses must travel more slowly in glass (and water) than in air.

But Huygens had no way of explaining how his impulses might explain different colours (his impulses had no regular frequency) and the dispersion of white light. Newton's theory was also able to explain the phenomenon of **polarisation**. Huygen's theory could not because he had only imagined *longitudinal* impulses. So the particle theory was largely favoured and remained so for more than a hundred years.

Fig. 3 Huygen's explanation of refraction

incident light

wavefront

secondary wavelets

air

water

This part of the wavefront slows down first and starts to be overtaken by the rest of the wave.

refracted light

2 a Write a summary of the evidence for the two theories of light that existed in the 18th century.
  b Was there any experimental evidence? What other evidence do you think there could have been with the apparatus available?
  c Can you think of a non-scientific reason for people preferring Newton's theories?

Diffraction and interference

Newton had observed a phenomenon that we now call Newton's Rings which is caused by the interference of light waves. Newton tried to explain the phenomenon by developing complex ideas of 'fitful' (oscillating) forces on the particles of light. This was the first admission that observations implied that light was associated with some wave-like properties.

'Newton's Rings'. An interference phenomenon first described in print by Robert Hooke in 1665.

Around 1800, Thomas Young (1773–1829) looked at the diffraction of a single colour of light from two small but close holes (Fig. 4). The light produces alternating areas of bright and dull intensity, which we now call interference 'fringes'. The two light beams interfered with each other.

Fig. 4 Young's 'double-slit' experiment

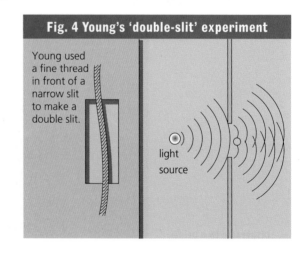

Young used a fine thread in front of a narrow slit to make a double slit.

light source

Interference of light produces maxima and minima of intensity called 'fringes'. The fringes from the blue light are closer together than the fringes from the red light. Young inferred from his experiment that each colour of light had its own wavelength.

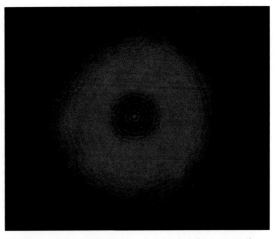

The Poisson Spot. This photo shows a bright spot at the centre of the shadow of a ball bearing. This was a big surprise to the particle-theory scientists that had ridiculed such an idea.

Interference between water ripples produces maxima and minima of wave amplitude.

Young turned to Huygens' idea, not Newton's particles, to explain what he saw. He added an important idea to Huygens' theory: that light of a single colour has a specific wavelength. This not only explained the interference patterns, but also how white light could be made up of different colours that appeared when dispersed by a prism or lens.

The French scientist Siméon Poisson (1781–1840) was an advocate of the particle theory of light. To outline how absurd he considered the wave theory, Poisson proved that if light was a wave then you could produce a bright spot at the centre of a circular shadow. This strategy backfired when the spot was observed and demonstrated in 1819. Particle theories of light could not hope to explain such a spot. Young's reconception of Huygens' waves of light became more popular than ever.

By 1850 it had been demonstrated that light was slower in water than in air. This finally buried any notion that light could be due to simple particles.

Key ideas

- Isaac Newton's particle theory of light was dominant throughout the 18th century. The particle theory supposed that different coloured light was due to different types of particle and that white light was an even mixture of these particles.

- The opposing wave theory proposed by Christiaan Huygens remained largely unsupported for over a hundred years.

The theory couldn't explain colour or polarisation because the theory relied on random, longitudinal wave motion.

- Young's famous 'double-slit' experiment demonstrates that light has a definite wave nature. Young suggested that each colour of light had a unique wavelength.

8.3 Electromagnetic waves

In 1872 James Clerk Maxwell (1831–1879) developed a set of equations that linked changes in electric fields with changes in magnetic fields. These equations followed on from Faraday's initial ideas about the transmission of electromagnetic effects, such as the deflection of a magnet by a current (Fig. 5). When Maxwell combined his equations together, he noticed that they described a travelling pattern, or wave, of electric and magnetic field strength (Fig. 6).

Fig. 6 Propagation of a light wave

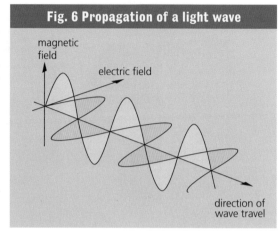

magnetic field

electric field

direction of wave travel

Fig. 5 Changing fields

Faraday demonstrated the link between electricity and magnetism

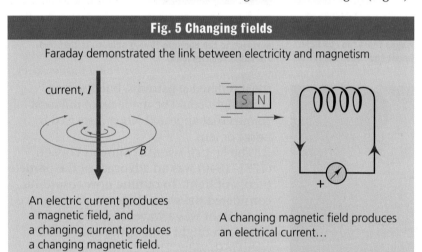

current, I

B

An electric current produces a magnetic field, and a changing current produces a changing magnetic field.

A changing magnetic field produces an electrical current…

Maxwell rearranged the equations and found that the speed of the waves of electric and magnetic field would travel with a speed c given by,

$$c = \sqrt{\frac{1}{\varepsilon_0 \mu_0}}$$

Where $\varepsilon_0 = 8.9 \times 10^{-12}$ F m^{-1} and $\mu_0 = 1.3 \times 10^{-6}$ H m^{-1} (both are known universal constants). Maxwell's value for c was exactly the same as the measured speed of light: 3×10^8 m s^{-1}. He was convinced that light must be a wave of electric and magnetic (electromagnetic) fields.

Fig. 7 Measuring the speed of light

Light travels very quickly; at 3.0×10^8 m s^{-1}. This makes it very difficult to measure. Early thinkers, including René Descartes, had imagined that light travelled instantaneously – with an infinite speed. Galileo Galilei, among others, suggested that light was merely fast. It proved to be so fast, that it wasn't measured on Earth until the 19th century. An American called Albert Michelson used two tricks to help to get around the difficulty of measuring such a fast speed. The *obvious* trick was to measure the time that light takes to travel over a reasonable distance: from mountain peak to mountain peak and then reflected back. The *clever* trick was to use a rapidly rotating drum made up of eight mirrors.

A pulse of light can be seen through the apparatus only if the drum has gone through precisely $^1/_8$ of a revolution by the time light travels to the neighbouring mountain and back. Any more or less than $^1/_8$ of a rotation, and the beam will reflect off to one side or the other.

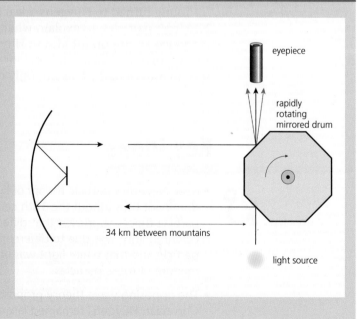

eyepiece

rapidly rotating mirrored drum

34 km between mountains

light source

3 In 1676, Ole Rømer estimated the speed of light by measuring the orbit time of one of Jupiter's moons.

a As the Earth is moving towards Jupiter, the orbit time of its moons appears to be shorter than when the Earth is moving away from Jupiter. Explain why.

b Explain how this could be used as a way to estimate the speed of light.

4 Michelson's rotating octagonal-drum experiment was set up on adjacent mountain peaks 34 kilometres apart. Calculate the revolutions per second of the octagonal drum when the light is seen through the apparatus.

The discovery of the electromagnetic spectrum opened up the possibilities of astronomical and domestic technology.

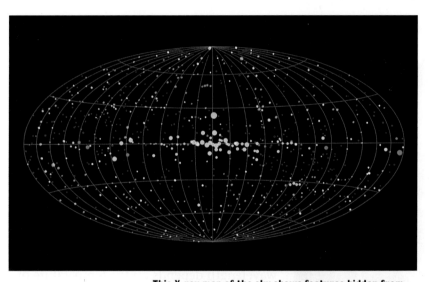

This X-ray map of the sky shows features hidden from the naked eye. The large green disc above the centre of the image is the brightest X-ray source in the sky. It may well be the site of a large black hole.

Maxwell's equation predicted waves of electromagnetic fields with a wide range of frequencies – frequencies much larger and smaller than that of visible light. About 15 years later, a German physicist called Heinrich Hertz found evidence for a radiation that spread out from sparks and travelled across his laboratory. He demonstrated that this radiation could be reflected, refracted and polarised. Hertz had discovered radio waves. In 1895, William Röntgen, also German, demonstrated the existence of radiation at the opposite end of the spectrum: X-rays (Fig. 8).

Maxwell's equations predicted something else – that the speed of light is constant in a vacuum. It doesn't matter if you, the observer, move at very high speed towards or away from a source of light. When you measure the speed of the light, you always get the same answer. That doesn't happen with *anything* else; it goes against all common sense. But, as Einstein said, 'common sense is nothing more than a deposit of prejudices.' (You can read more

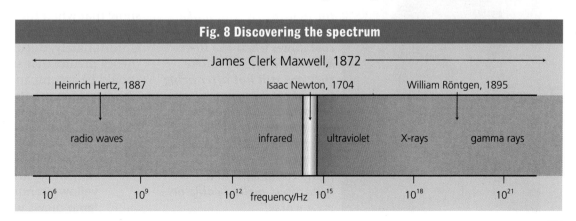

Fig. 8 Discovering the spectrum

James Clerk Maxwell, 1872

Heinrich Hertz, 1887   Isaac Newton, 1704   William Röntgen, 1895

radio waves   infrared   ultraviolet   X-rays   gamma rays

10^6 10^9 10^{12} frequency/Hz 10^{15} 10^{18} 10^{21}

about how Einstein resolved this problem in Chapter 12.)

Wave theory had become an established idea. Once ideas become established then they become hard to shift. So when the wave theory of light produced a wrong prediction, people found it hard to drop the theory.

 5 Explain the importance of the work of Hertz to the work of Maxwell.

Key ideas

- Light is a wave of electric and magnetic fields.

- Heinrich Hertz was the first to discover Maxwell's predicted electromagnetic waves outside the visible part of the spectrum.

- The speed of the electromagnetic waves was predicted by Maxwell as being:

$$c = \sqrt{\frac{1}{\varepsilon_0 \mu_0}}$$ where ε_0 and μ_0 are well known universal constants.

8.4 The problem with waves

'We have to take care with the lighting rig and make sure that it is given time to cool down when the lights are turned off. Of course they are still hot after being turned off, but more importantly they are still emitting energy in the dangerous infrared region. Being careless with the lights could lead to a hazardous melted cable or even worse!'

Scientists gaining confidence in the wave theory of light, still had an annoying problem to deal with. According to the theory, everything in the universe should be emitting bright ultraviolet light!

Filament light-bulbs shine because they are so hot that oscillating charged particles within the material emit light in the visible part of the electromagnetic spectrum. All objects emit energy in the form of electromagnetic radiation across a range of wavelengths. Experimental observations show that the intensity of a particular wavelength depends on the temperature of the object. This emitted radiation is called **black-body radiation** (Fig. 9). (Strictly speaking, a 'black body' is a perfect absorber that does not *reflect* any light.)

Observations of black-body radiation show that when the wavelength is small, intensity and energy output is small. Unfortunately, calculations based on wave theory predict that small wavelengths should be accompanied by a large intensity. The discrepancy between theory and observation at low wavelengths is called the **ultraviolet catastrophe** (Fig. 10).

6 Explain why an electric heater glows red, an electric lamp glows with a yellow-orange light, and a welding lamp glows with bluish white light.

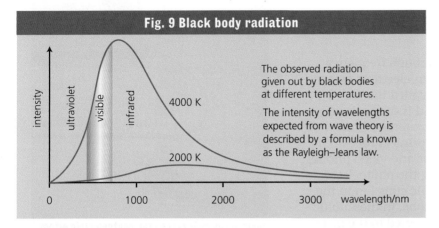

Fig. 9 Black body radiation

intensity | wavelength/nm

ultraviolet | visible | infrared

4000 K

2000 K

0   1000   2000   3000

The observed radiation given out by black bodies at different temperatures.

The intensity of wavelengths expected from wave theory is described by a formula known as the Rayleigh–Jeans law.

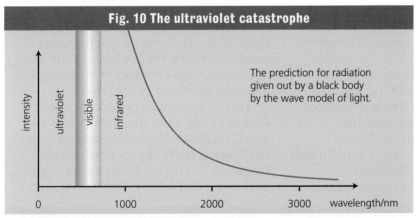

Fig. 10 The ultraviolet catastrophe

intensity

ultraviolet | visible | infrared

0   1000   2000   3000   wavelength/nm

The prediction for radiation given out by a black body by the wave model of light.

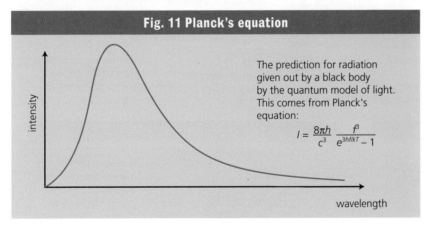

Fig. 11 Planck's equation

intensity

wavelength

The prediction for radiation given out by a black body by the quantum model of light. This comes from Planck's equation:

$$I = \frac{8\pi h}{c^3} \frac{f^3}{e^{3hf/kT} - 1}$$

The accidental birth of the quantum

In 1900, Max Planck set out to create an equation that accurately described black-body radiation. When he finally succeeded it took him another two months to work out what his equation implied.

It seemed to Planck that his equation described the energy of the electromagnetic field changing in lumps, or **quanta**, of energy instead of the steady and continuous flow expected of a wave phenomenon. The important point for Planck was that the maths 'worked' (Fig. 11). He didn't believe that energy really behaved in such a way.

The idea that light energy didn't spread out evenly over a wavefront, that it *really did* exist in tiny localised packets called **photons**, was seriously suggested by Albert Einstein. Einstein found that this idea helped explain another scientific puzzle: the photoelectric effect.

Key ideas

- The radiation of black-bodies (non-reflective emitters) has a characteristic wavelength–intensity curve that depends on the temperature of the body.

- The wave theory of light could not account for the character of black-body radiation.

- Planck introduced the idea of quantising electromagnetic energy to explain black-body radiation.

8.5 The photoelectric effect

When light of a high enough frequency hits a metal surface, then electrons escape from the metal. This is called the **photoelectric effect** and is the basis of most modern imaging systems – from photocopiers and laser printers to miniature video cameras and video phones.

It's worth contrasting the photoelectric effect with the thermionic emission in the cathode of a television tube. In thermionic emission, energy is transferred to the metal by heating it, and with enough thermal energy, electrons can escape. In the photoelectric effect, the source of energy is light.

Puzzlingly, for the scientist who first discovered the effect (in 1890), the light must be above a certain frequency. Below this **threshold frequency**, nothing happens regardless of the brightness (intensity) of the light. Further experiments showed that above the threshold frequency, a *brighter* light releases more

Modern cameras rely on the photoelectric effect.

electrons, but makes no difference to the speed of the fastest ones. On the other hand, increasing the *frequency* of the light releases the same number of electrons, but increases the speed of the fastest.

This all seemed rather odd. A steady flow of energy onto the metal ought to provide a steady stream of escaping electrons. A faster energy flow (higher frequency *or* brighter light) ought to give both more and faster electrons (Fig. 12).

Fig. 12 Photoelectric effects

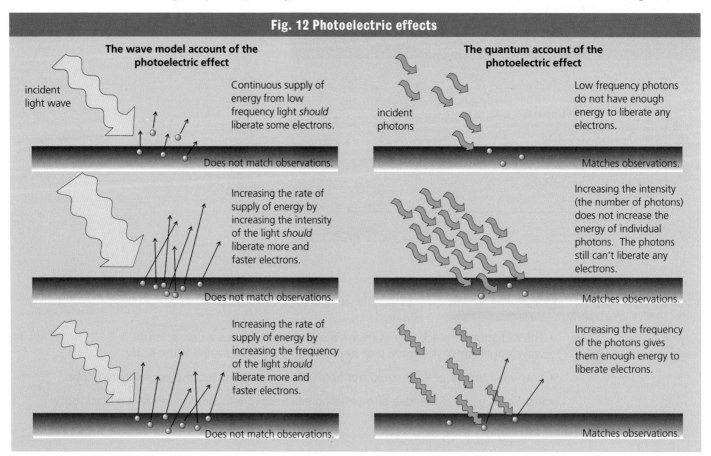

The wave model account of the photoelectric effect

incident light wave

Continuous supply of energy from low frequency light *should* liberate some electrons.

Does not match observations.

Increasing the rate of supply of energy by increasing the intensity of the light *should* liberate more and faster electrons.

Does not match observations.

Increasing the rate of supply of energy by increasing the frequency of the light *should* liberate more and faster electrons.

Does not match observations.

The quantum account of the photoelectric effect

incident photons

Low frequency photons do not have enough energy to liberate any electrons.

Matches observations.

Increasing the intensity (the number of photons) does not increase the energy of individual photons. The photons still can't liberate any electrons.

Matches observations.

Increasing the frequency of the photons gives them enough energy to liberate electrons.

Matches observations.

It took the genius of Einstein to come up with an explanation that works. He used the idea that light does not provide a steady energy flow, but a 'lumpy' energy flow. The observations can be explained if you imagine the energy arriving at the metal surface in small packages: photons.

The energy of a photon is related to its frequency by the equation:

$E = hf,$

where h is a constant, called Planck's constant (6.6×10^{-34} J s). Like ε_0 and μ_0, h is one of nature's fundamental constants.

Each electron needs a certain minimum amount of energy, W, to escape from the metal surface. This energy is called the **work function** of the metal. The escape of an electron is caused by the absorption of one photon with enough energy. If the photon frequency is below a certain value (if hf is less than W) the electron cannot escape. This is consistent with the observation that the freqency must be

above a certain value before the photoelectric effect takes place at all.

Throwing more photons (brighter or higher intensity light) at the metal will not help if none of the photons has got enough energy. That is why the brightness of light does not influence the energy gained by individual electrons.

If the photons have a high enough frequency (if hf is bigger than W), then not only can they set electrons free, but there is some energy left over. Some of that energy can be carried away by the electrons in the form of kinetic energy. That is why increasing the frequency of light increases the maximum velocity of escaping electrons.

Every aspect of Einstein's theory (formulated in 1905) was confirmed by a famous set of experiments carried out by Robert Millikan in 1915 (Fig. 13). Much later, when the theory was finally accepted, Einstein was awarded the Nobel Prize for his explanation of the effect.

Fig. 13 Millikan's photoelectric experiment

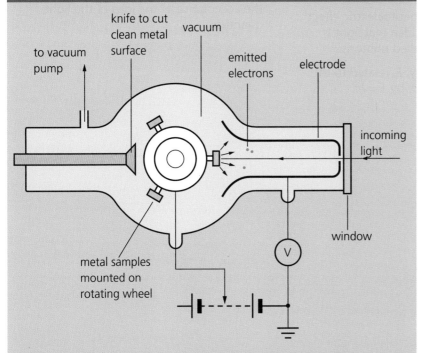

Millikan took an ordinary photocell and made the collecting electrode negative with respect to the photocathode. This meant that the escaping electrons would be repelled. Only the most energetic would reach the electrode. As the potential difference is increased, the current of escaping electrons drops.
At the 'stopping voltage', the current is zero. The kinetic energy of the fastest electrons can be deduced from the stopping voltage using:
kinetic energy lost = work done = charge × potential difference

Fig. 14 Stopping voltage

photon energy = min. energy needed to liberate electron
+ max. electron kinetic energy

$hf = W + \text{K.E.}_{max}$
$\text{K.E.}_{max} = hf - W$

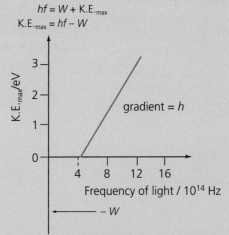

The maximum kinetic energy plotted against frequency of light, from Millikan's experiment. This shows exactly what Einstein predicted: that the maximum energy of released electrons is proportional to the frequency of light.
The constant of proportionality (the gradient of the graph) is equal to h.

8.6 Waves and particles

Atoms can only have discrete energy levels. Atoms move to higher energy levels by absorbing a lump of electromagnetic radiation. When atoms fall to lower energy levels, they emit a lump of electromagnetic radiation. Matter and light exchange energy in a lumpy, or quantum, way; not in a continuous way. This is the starting point of one of the most successful fields in 20th century physics: quantum mechanics.

Is light a wave or does it come in lumps? The answer is: both! We can model light on anything we please – ripples on a pond, or tiny cannonballs. Just remember that light *isn't* ripples on a pond and *isn't* tiny cannonballs. Light is what it is, and we can predict how it behaves in particular situations by modelling it on something else that we are familiar with.

Light shows all the behaviour of waves – reflection, refraction and diffraction. But its energy travels in discrete packages like a particle. Sometimes you get the right answers when you describe light as a wave, and sometimes you only get the right answers when you think about it as a flow of particles. These models are not alternatives, but two *complementary* parts of a fuller model known as **wave–particle duality**.

Key ideas

- Wave theory could not explain many aspects of the photoelectric effect.

- Einstein explained the photoelectric effect by taking seriously the idea that light is quantised in packets called photons.

- Photons have an energy, *E*, related to the frequency of the light, *f*, by $E = hf$.

- Millikan's experiment demonstrated the predictions of Einstein's theory. This led to the acceptance of the idea of the light quantum.

9 Microworlds

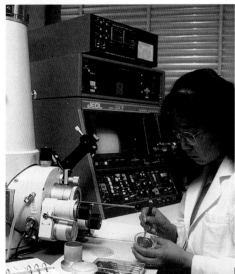

'The electron microscope is invaluable in our research on viruses. For the first time, we can magnify images to the point where we can actually see the structure of the virus. Seeing the detail of how HIV physically attacks and then uses the body's biological machinery is a big help in our ongoing research. Ordinary optical microscopes could never show us such detail: they would only produce a blur.'

There is more to life than meets the eye The quality of our eye lenses and of the cells on our retinas put limits on what we can directly see. Microscopes take us into new worlds and tell us about the existence of whole ecosystems of creatures, from plankton to bacteria.

Diffraction of light blurs the images of even the best optical microscopes. Electron microscopes can take us deeper still into the microworld – down to images of the viruses which cause infections from flu to HIV. Electron microscopes are standard tools in the fight against viral disease.

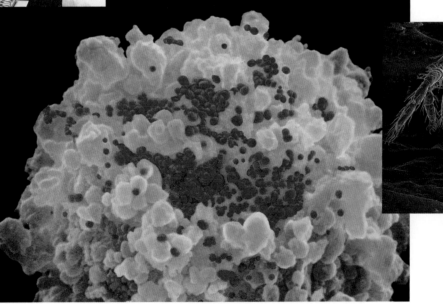

This picture from an electron microscope shows a cluster of HIV (in red) budding away from a T-lymphocyte blood cell (a part of the immune system). Magnification = 6000.

A mite walking over skin seen through an electron microscope. Magnification = 150.

9.1 Learning objectives

After working through this chapter, you should be able to:

- **describe** the wave–particle nature of electrons;

- **calculate** the energy, momentum and wavelength of electrons;

- **describe** the behaviour of low intensity beams of electrons in terms of probabilistic descriptions;

- **explain** how the wavelength of high energy electrons allows much greater magnification than is possible with light;

- **explain** the principles of a transmission electron microscope;

- **explain** the principles of a scanning tunnelling microscope.

9.2 The limits of wavelength

No matter how carefully the lens makers might work, there is a certain size below which light microscopes can tell us nothing more. There is a size at which it is impossible to distinguish between two objects – to tell if they are two or just one. This is known as **resolving** the objects. The limiting factor in resolving is the wavelength of the light. Though light is perceived to travel in straight lines, it behaves like other waves. Waves spread around obstacles – they *diffract* (Fig. 1). The effect is strongest when the obstacle is the same size as the wavelength of the waves, or smaller. Diffraction destroys clear images.

The wavelength of light is about 5×10^{-7} m. A pair of objects less than about a millionth of metre apart will blur into one, no matter how many times their image is magnified.

Fig. 1 The problem with diffraction

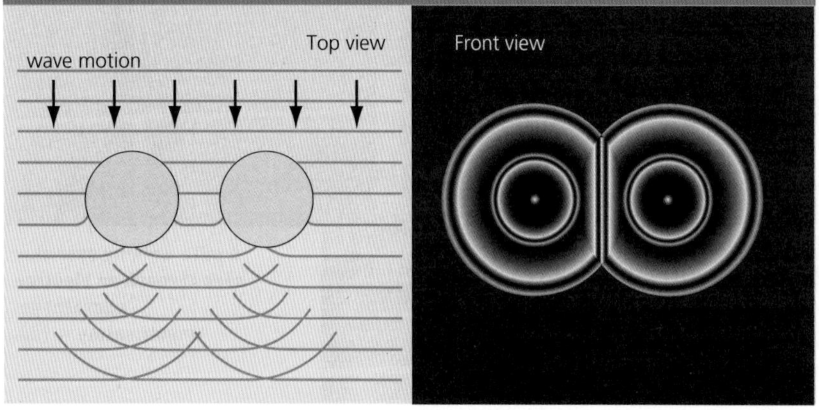

wave motion

Top view

Front view

 1 **Why have optical microscopes been more useful in the development of modern medicine than they have in the development of particle ideas of matter?**

Momentum and wavelength
Photons have both wave and particle properties (see Chapter 8). When a photon collides with an electron, the electron recoils: photons have momentum. If light has some particle properties, do particles of matter, such as electrons, have some wave properties?

In 1923, Louis de Broglie (a French prince, whose name is pronounced 'de Broy-lee') tried out this idea as part of his studies for a doctorate. Some of his examiners were stunned by his ideas, and weren't sure that de Broglie should get his PhD. One of the examiners sent the work to Einstein, who wasn't afraid of novelty, and de Broglie shortly became a doctor as well as a prince.

Louis de Broglie suggested that particles were associated with a certain wavelength given by:

$$\lambda = \frac{h}{p} \quad \text{or} \quad p = \frac{h}{\lambda}$$

where p is the particle's momentum and h is Planck's constant. This equation is known as the **de Broglie relationship**.

2 **Electrons from the electron gun in a TV travel with speeds of, roughly, 10^7 m s^{-1}. What is the wavelength of these electrons, according to de Broglie? ($h = 6.6 \times 10^{-34}$ J s)**

In 1912, the scientist Niels Bohr suggested that electrons in an atom were restricted to certain orbits. He had suggested this to fit observations of the emission of light from atoms and as a way to resolve the problems of Rutherford's nuclear model of the atom (see *Physics Core* book, Chapter 11). Bohr guessed that electrons were in orbit around the nucleus *only* in allowed energy levels at corresponding distances from the nucleus. An electron in an atom could never have an 'in-between' energy and could never stay at an in-between distance, but could only jump from level to level.

Louis de Broglie's idea fitted very well with Bohr's – it justified the model for electron orbits as 'standing matter waves'. Imagine that electrons behave like standing waves on a string, but with the string looped into a circle. There are only certain lengths of loop in which standing waves of a particular wavelength can join up to make a circle.

At certain frequencies, the vibration of the loop creates a standing wave. At most frequencies, the waves in the loop cancel each other out as they travel around.

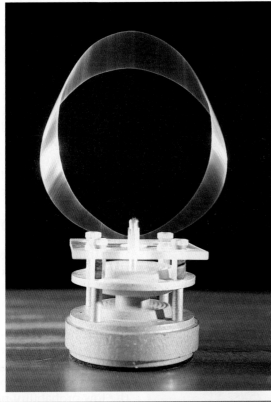

Electrons with a wavelength of 2×10^{-11} m diffracting through graphite. The outer ring is due to rows of atoms 1.2×10^{-10} m apart.

Electron diffraction and interference

In 1927, de Broglie's suggestion that electrons might behave like waves was confirmed. A Scottish scientist called George Thomson (son of the J.J. Thomson who first discovered the existence of electron 'particles') fired high speed electrons at gold foil. The emerging electron beam varied in intensity like light from a diffraction grating. That is, the atoms of gold and the spaces between them acted as a diffraction grating and the electrons were behaving like waves. Young's 'double slit' experiment, which had once gone to show that light had wave-like properties, was soon duplicated with electrons (Fig. 2). The spreading electron waves combine together, to produce patterns of interference.

If we think of a beam of electrons as a wave motion, like waves on water, then it is not too difficult for us to imagine waves going through one slit and interfering with waves going through the other slit. But even when electrons pass through a double slit one by one, they still form an interference pattern!

Fig. 2 Diffraction of electrons

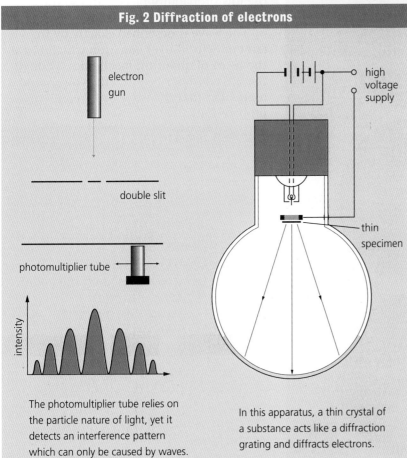

electron gun

double slit

photomultiplier tube

intensity

high voltage supply

thin specimen

The photomultiplier tube relies on the particle nature of light, yet it detects an interference pattern which can only be caused by waves.

In this apparatus, a thin crystal of a substance acts like a diffraction grating and diffracts electrons.

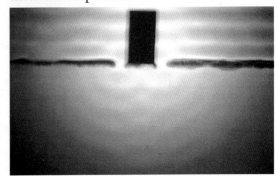

In this water ripple tank you can see that a double source of waves produces radiating regions of no amplitude alternating with regions of high amplitude.

93

If an electron passes through the slits on its own, there seems to be no other wave for it to interfere with. Yet, in time, as electrons feed through the system, an interference pattern appears which is just the same as the pattern produced by a short burst of a high intensity beam of electrons.

When light is diffracted through two slits, alternating patterns of high and low intensity are produced. Electrons behave in the same way when they pass through a double slit.

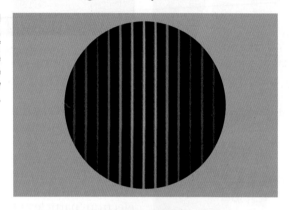

Electron diffraction. The electrons arrive one by one, but the picture builds up into familiar bands of high and low intensity.

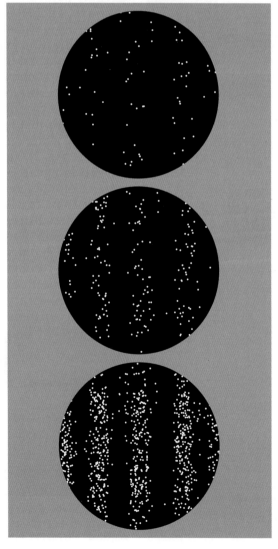

The pattern of diffraction produced by a double slit is very different from the pattern of diffraction produced by a single slit. It is as if a solitary electron can tell the difference between a double slit and a single slit system. An individual electron, if it is a 'localised' particle, can only pass through one slit, and has no way of interacting with the second slit. We have to conclude that each electron effectively does pass through *both* slits – we must remember that electrons are simply not just particles.

Waves of probability

Physicists talk about waves that govern the probability of the position of particles (Fig. 3). It is each electron's 'probability wave' that emerges from both slits and produces interference. The probability of the electron being at a particular point when it hits the detecting screen is equal to the square of the wave's amplitude at that point. More electrons accumulate, one by one, at the high probability places than at the low probability places, and so the interference pattern builds up.

The wave is described exactly by the famous Schrödinger equation which lies at the heart of quantum mechanics. Though the wave is described exactly, you should remember that the wave only represents probabilities.

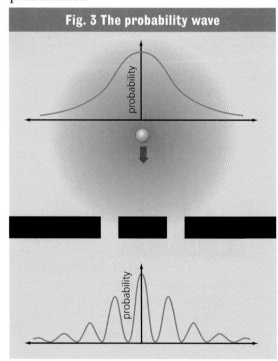

Fig. 3 The probability wave

Key ideas

- Diffraction is a natural limit on the resolution of an image.

- To resolve (distinguish between) objects in an image, the waves used to make the image need to have a wavelength on the same order of size (or smaller) than the objects.

- Particles have wave-like properties. The wavelength associated with a particle of momentum p is given by de Broglie's relationship:

$$\lambda = \frac{h}{p}$$

where h is Planck's constant.

- The waves associated with particles describe the probability of the particle occupying one point.

9.3 Ten thousand times smaller

Optical or light microscopes work by transmitted light (shining through the object) or by reflected light (shining off the object). They can resolve two points that are about a millionth of a metre across and a millionth of a metre apart. Diffraction blurs the light from anything smaller.

An electron microscope takes advantage of the fact that electrons have a much smaller wavelength than light when they are moving at speed. The smaller wavelength allows electron beams to resolve much smaller objects.

A transmission electron microscope (TEM) uses a beam of electrons travelling through a thin object (Fig. 4). Electric and magnetic fields focus the electron beam just as glass lenses focus light. Electrons in a TV are also steered by electric and magnetic fields. And in both electron microscopes and TVs, electrons are first accelerated to high speed in an electron gun.

Just how small can we get λ to be? Remember that the smaller it is, the better the resolution. The de Broglie relationship tells us that,

$$\lambda = \frac{h}{p} \quad \text{or} \quad p = \frac{h}{\lambda}$$

The momentum of an electron is related to its speed, which in turn depends on the energy used to accelerate it in the first place. The energy, E, given to an electron, charge e, by the electron gun with voltage

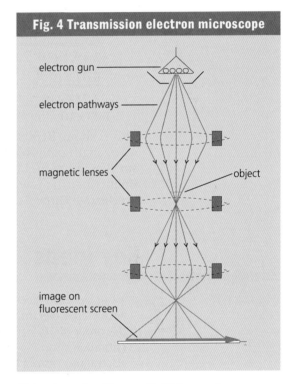

Fig. 4 Transmission electron microscope

electron gun

electron pathways

magnetic lenses

object

image on fluorescent screen

V, is given by, $E = e \times V$. This can be equated to the electron's final kinetic energy:

$$\tfrac{1}{2}mv^2 = eV$$
$$m^2v^2 = 2meV$$

Momentum is mass times velocity ($p = mv$) so,

$$p^2 = 2meV$$
$$p = \sqrt{2meV}$$

95

We can substitute this into the de Broglie relationship, giving:

$$\lambda = \frac{h}{\sqrt{2meV}}$$

The wavelength of the electrons depends on only the variable V, the potential difference applied to the electron gun, because h, m and e are all constants. With a potential difference of 100 V, what wavelength do the resulting electrons have?

$h = 6.63 \times 10^{-34}$ J s, $m = 9.1 \times 10^{-31}$ kg, $e = 1.6 \times 10^{-19}$ C

Putting these numbers into the formula:

$$\lambda = \frac{h}{\sqrt{2meV}}$$

$$= \frac{6.63 \times 10^{-34} \text{ J s}}{\sqrt{2 \times 9.1 \times 10^{-31} \text{ kg} \times 1.6 \times 10^{-19} \text{ C} \times 100}}$$

$$= \frac{6.63 \times 10^{-34}}{\sqrt{2.912 \times 10^{-47}}} \text{ m}$$

$$= 1.23 \times 10^{-10} \text{ m}$$

This is about 10 000 times smaller than the wavelength of visible light – almost as small as atoms and the spacing between them. And that is with electrons accelerated through just 100 V. Higher voltages applied to the electron gun can give faster electrons, and even better potential resolving power. Electron microscopes can, in theory, take us into the world of atoms.

Unfortunately, transmission electron microscopes cannot produce images of atoms. The samples being viewed cannot always be reduced to a few atoms thick, so multiple and complex diffraction destroys the clarity of the image. Difficulty in achieving precision in the lens system (lens aberration), and vibrations of the electron microscope, also make it impossible to detect individual atoms.

3 Use de Broglie's relationship to work out:
  a The wavelength of an electron moving at 'thermal' speeds – the speed of random motion of electrons in a coin in your purse or pocket, which is about 10^6 m s^{-1}.
  b The wavelength of an electron accelerated to an energy of 1 keV.

4 What accelerating voltage would be required to view molecules 10^{-9} m across?

Key ideas

- A transmission electron microscope uses accelerated electrons to resolve objects of the order of 10^{-10} m, but practical problems (vibrations, sample thickness, lens aberration) restrict the resolving power.

- Electrons accelerated through a 100 V potential difference have a wavelength that is 10 000 times smaller than that of visible electromagnetic waves.

9.4 Tunnelling electrons

There is one more consequence of 'matter waves' that underpins all modern electronics and allows us to see images of individual atoms.

Many electrons exist in atoms where they are not free. They need to gain energy in order to escape. They have negative potential energy. If you picture potential energy as a graph, you can think of the electron trapped in a potential hole (Fig. 5). If you also imagine the electron as a particle then the probability of finding it outside the confines of its potential 'hole' is zero.

However, picturing the electron as governed by a probability wave leads to a different result, because the wave does not end at the sides of the hole. The wave equation gives a value of probability that

Fig. 5 Trapped in a potential hole

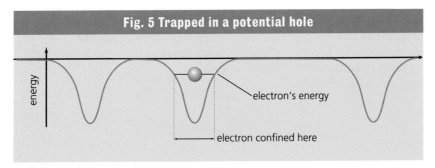

tails off very quickly with distance outside the potential well. The amplitude of the probability wave dies away quickly, but it is still not zero inside neighbouring atoms in energetically allowable regions. That means that there is a small probability that the electron could actually exist in the neighbouring atom (Fig. 6). It could jump through the barrier of the potential walls. This happens, and it is called **quantum tunnelling**. It is an important part of the conduction process in **semiconductor** technology. This process of tunnelling also explains how alpha particles escape from the nucleus during radioactive decay (see Chapter 4).

Fig. 6 Tunnelling through

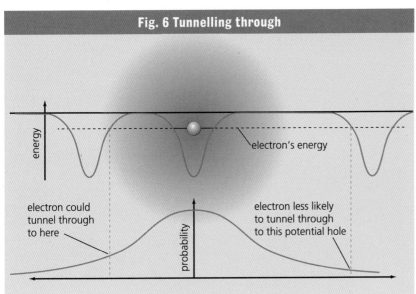

The scanning tunnelling electron microscope

If one atom is held very close to another atom, then there is a chance that electrons could tunnel from one atom to the other. If one atom is pulled away slightly then the flow of tunnelling electrons drops off very quickly. This means that the position of

Fig. 7 Scanning tunnelling electron microscope

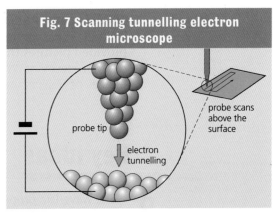

atoms can be accurately sensed. This is the basis of the scanning tunnelling electron microscope (STM).

An STM has a probe with a single atom at the end (Fig. 7). This scans across the surface of a sample, and electrons tunnel between probe and sample creating a current that is big enough to detect. Where probe and sample atoms are close together, the current is bigger. (The probe has a small voltage applied to it, to encourage electron tunnelling.) At last – images of individual atoms.

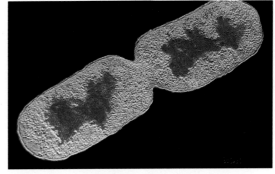

Magnification = 17 500. An ordinary transmission electron microscope can show the genetic material in this bacteria (in red), but ...

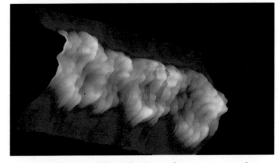

... a scanning tunnelling electron microscope can show the structure of that genetic material. Here you can clearly see the twisted double strands that form DNA. Magnification = 2 000 000.

Smaller and smaller

Each new magnifying instrument has provided pictures that are beyond the reach of its predecessor. We can now examine images of objects way beyond the reach of our direct vision. That is something that physics does for us: it extends out perception far beyond our senses into new microworlds.

Key ideas

- The wave-like properties of electrons means that they can move from one atom to another, even though there is a potential energy barrier between them. This is called quantum tunnelling.

- Scanning tunnelling electron microscopes use the phenomenon of quantum tunnelling as a precise way of sensing the position of atoms.

10 Steam-driven empires

The relationship between science and technology is a complicated thing. Sometimes, as in the case of steam engines, the technology develops and only then do the scientists move in to study what's happening. From the study of steam engines came the science of thermodynamics, and out of the science of thermodynamics, the principles of refrigeration emerged.

Technologies like the steam engine and the refrigerator can have an impact that's just too big to measure. They change the world for ever, transforming individual lives – even having huge effects on birth rates, life expectancy and the distribution of population.

The human story of the foundation of the USA has been romanticised and criticised, but no one disputes the huge part that technology played. It was the railroads that carried the drifting and settling population across the vast continent...

10.1 Learning objectives

After working through this chapter, you should be able to:

- **relate** the energy transferred thermally into and out of a system to the work that it does and to changes in internal energy;

- **understand** the usefulness and shortcomings of the ideal gas model;

- **calculate** the work done by an ideal gas in expanding against constant pressure;

- **understand** the distinction between adiabatic and isothermal changes.

10.2 Equilibrium

The first steam engines were built to solve the very practical and very expensive problem of pumping water out of mines. They were quite simple and extremely inefficient. For driving heavy machinery, horses were better value for money. Then James Watt developed a way of transferring more of the energy from the burning fuel to the motion of the pistons. Watt sold his new machines to mill owners by

Fig. 1 Energy transfers

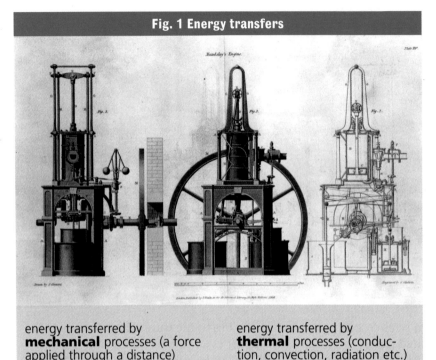

energy transferred by **mechanical** processes (a force applied through a distance)	energy transferred by **thermal** processes (conduction, convection, radiation etc.)
The product of force and distance. This is often called work, or work done.	Note that to avoid confusion, we shall not be calling this heat, as internal energy is often called heat too.

Fig. 2 Thermal transfer of energy

water T_2

$T_1 > T_2$

energy transferred by conduction, convection and radiation

T_1

T_3

T_1

T_2

energy transferred by conduction
$T_1 < T_2$

T_1

T_2

$T_1 = T_2 = T_3$ (thermal equilibrium)
no energy transferred thermally

comparing them to horses – in terms of 'horsepower' (745.7 watts = 1 horsepower).

As engines became smaller, it became possible to mount them on wheels. There was huge investment in the new 'locomotives'. Rail networks spread, cities built stations with elaborate architecture, and almost every village had its own little station on a branch line. At the same time, scientists were trying to establish a consistent theory that would describe and predict the processes behind all these new wonders. The science of mechanical and thermal energy transfers is called **thermodynamics** (Fig. 1).

Modern thermodynamics begins with the idea of thermal equilibrium. If a body is in thermal equilibrium with its surroundings then there is no net thermal transfer of energy into or out of it. If two objects have different temperatures and are left to themselves, then energy will pass between them – they will not be in thermal equilibrium. The raging fire of a boiler and the water that is poured through it are not in thermal equilibrium. There is a temperature difference, and there is energy transfer from the higher temperature material to the lower temperature material by a thermal process such as conduction or convection (Fig. 2).

1 Are you in thermal equilibrium with:
a your neighbour?
b the heater in the room when it is on?
c the rest of your surroundings?

Energy and temperature

If we know the temperature of two objects then we can predict which way energy will be thermally transferred between them. If you touch a hot wire or a hot steel girder, you will get burned. Energy will flow to your skin. But if you try heating a wire and a girder, you will have to provide much more energy to the girder than to the wire in order to notice any change. Both objects can experience exactly the same change in their total internal energy, but the temperature of the wire changes much more than the temperature of the girder.

Changes to the internal energy of an object are related to temperature changes,

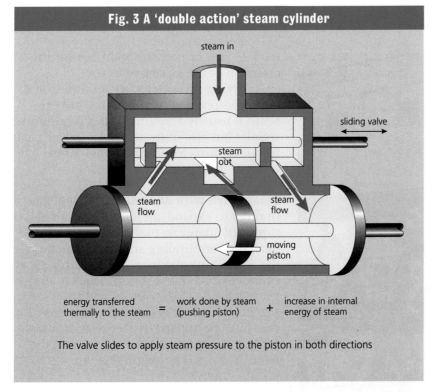

Fig. 3 A 'double action' steam cylinder

steam in

sliding valve

steam out

steam flow

steam flow

moving piston

energy transferred thermally to the steam = work done by steam (pushing piston) + increase in internal energy of steam

The valve slides to apply steam pressure to the piston in both directions

The first law of thermodynamics

The boiler of a steam engine supplies energy to a mass of water which becomes steam. The steam continues to get hotter (its internal energy increases). Then the steam does work, pushing on the piston in the cylinder (Fig. 3). Ultimately, the steam has both risen in temperature and done work on something.

It wasn't until after national and international rail networks were built all across Europe, that James Joule showed the direct and simple link between thermal energy transfer and mechanical work. This link is summed up in the first law of thermodynamics:

The total increase in internal energy of a body together with the work done by that body must be the same as the energy thermally transferred to it.

energy transferred thermally = work done + change in internal energy

$$\Delta Q = \Delta W + \Delta U$$

This agrees with the principle of conservation of energy, which says that energy cannot be created or destroyed. In fact, the first law of thermodynamics *is* the principle of conservation of energy, applied to processes of thermal energy transfer.

but they are also related to its mass, and to the nature of its particles and the forces between them. Internal energy and temperature are not the same thing.

 2 a If you sit in a bath of cold water then the internal energy of the water increases. Explain why.

b If you sit in the Atlantic Ocean its temperature does not rise as much as that of the water in the bath. Explain why.

 3 Is it ever possible for steam to do more work (ΔW) than the total energy that is supplied to it (ΔQ)? Explain your answer.

Key ideas

 • The first law of thermodynamics is:

The total increase in internal energy of a body together with the work done by that body must be the same as the energy thermally transferred to it.

This can be written as:

$\Delta Q = \Delta W + \Delta U$.

10.3 Expansion

The expansion of the white American population into new western territories pushed the existing population out of the way. This picture, taken in 1886, shows Apaches being transported from their native Arizona to an exile in Florida. The Apache leader Geronimo is third from the right at the front.

Railways quickly spread to the rest of the world. In the early days of the 1800s, few people of European origin had travelled by land into the western half of the USA. By the middle of the century, pressures of poverty had driven some wagon trains westwards. But it was the railways that allowed a huge new population to spread into the near-empty spaces, like a burst of steam from a valve on a boiler.

Real and ideal gases

Scientists imagine an **ideal gas** in which there are no attractive forces and in which the particles themselves have no volume. The reason for this flight of fancy is that it is simple to predict the behaviour of an ideal gas, and real gases behave like ideal gases in many circumstances. In fact, you would have to make quite precise measurements to notice the difference between a real gas and the imaginary 'ideal' one. The forces of attraction between particles in a gas are very weak.

When any gas expands, it must do work to push surrounding material, usually the air, out of the way. A real gas must also do work to pull its particles apart against the direction of the attractive forces. Quantifying this extra work involves some fairly complicated mathematics, but the result is usually very small. So it is not only simpler but also quite adequate, in practical terms, to think about gas behaviour in terms of ideal gases.

Doing work with an expanding ideal gas

In order to expand, an ideal gas needs a supply of energy so that it can do work and push the surrounding atmosphere out of the way. Think about an ideal gas in a cylinder which has a piston. There is air on the other side of the piston, and the pressure of the air is constant. The force, F, that must be applied by the ideal gas as it expands must be equal to the force of the atmosphere on the piston (Fig. 4):

$$F = pA$$

Work is the product of force and distance, so the work that must be done by the gas in the cylinder when it expands is equal to the force with which it pushes back the external atmosphere multiplied by the distance through which it pushes the piston:

$$W = F \, \Delta x$$
$$= p \, A \, \Delta x$$
$$= p \, \Delta V$$

where ΔV is the extra volume through which the gas expands. This is a general relationship which applies to any expansion of an ideal gas against a constant external pressure.

4 a Why does the formula $W = p\Delta V$ not apply to real gases? Explain why the formula is still useful for describing real gases.
b In what circumstances would the formula not describe the behaviour of a real gas?

Energy for expansion

Energy is required if work is to be done. An ideal gas must do work to expand, to push air out of the way. The first law of

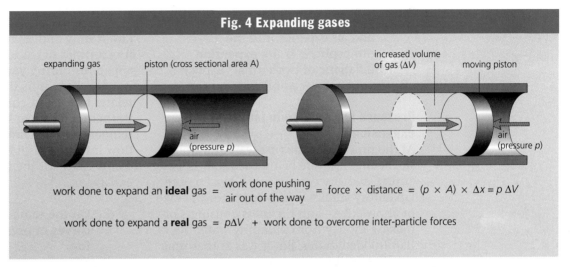

Fig. 4 Expanding gases

expanding gas

piston (cross sectional area A)

air (pressure *p*)

increased volume of gas (ΔV)

moving piston

air (pressure *p*)

work done to expand an **ideal** gas $=\dfrac{\text{work done pushing}}{\text{air out of the way}}=$ force $\times$ distance $= (p \times A) \times \Delta x = p\,\Delta V$

work done to expand a **real** gas $= p\Delta V$ + work done to overcome inter-particle forces

thermodynamics tells us that there are two possible sources of energy for this work: the internal energy of the gas, and energy transferred to the gas thermally ($\Delta W = \Delta Q - \Delta U$).

Very often expansion will take from both sources of energy. For an ideal gas, there are two extreme cases (Fig. 5). At one extreme, all of the energy comes from the internal energy of the gas: this is called **adiabatic** expansion. At the other extreme, all of the energy is transferred into the gas from outside: this is **isothermal** expansion.

In adiabatic change, the gas is effectively isolated from the outside world. There is no energy thermally transferred into or out of it; ΔQ is zero. In order to expand, it must take energy from its own internal energy.

The change in internal energy of the gas results in a change in its temperature, so adiabatic expansion provides a way of cooling a gas. In adiabatic expansion, $\Delta W = -\Delta U$.

In isothermal expansion, the temperature stays constant. For an ideal gas, constant temperature means constant internal energy; $\Delta U = 0$. Expansion is only possible if there is a supply of energy, from outside the gas, to match the work being done. In this case, the first law of thermodynamics says that, as there is no change in internal energy, energy thermally transferred into the gas from an outside source is equal to the work done by the gas. In isothermal expansion, $\Delta W = \Delta Q$.

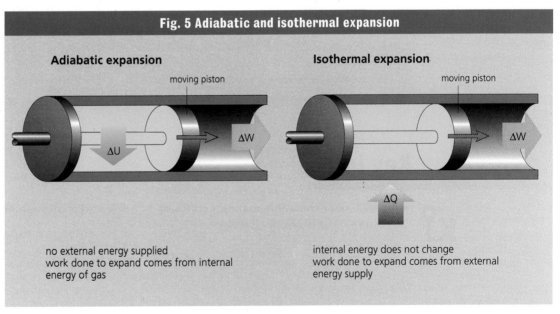

Fig. 5 Adiabatic and isothermal expansion

Adiabatic expansion

moving piston

ΔU

ΔW

no external energy supplied
work done to expand comes from internal energy of gas

Isothermal expansion

moving piston

ΔW

ΔQ

internal energy does not change
work done to expand comes from external energy supply

5 **You press the valve on a bicycle tyre and air expands into the atmosphere. Is the expansion adiabatic or isothermal? Explain your answer as fully as you can.**

Pressure and volume in isothermal expansion

At the time when the first water-pumping steam engines were being tried out, nobody anticipated any connection between pure laboratory studies – knowledge for the sake of knowledge – and the messy business of making money from pumping water out of half-flooded mines. But it was at that time that Robert Boyle was studying the behaviour of gases, and discovered a pattern of behaviour that we now call Boyle's law.

Boyle's law states that the pressure of a fixed mass of gas at constant temperature is inversely proportional to its volume. The relationship can be expressed in graph form (Fig. 6).

Notice the careful wording of Boyle's law. It only applies to a fixed mass of gas – if quantities of gas leak in or out of your apparatus during your experiment, you will not get the graphs shown. Boyle's law also relates to a gas at constant temperature – to isothermal change. To keep the temperature constant, energy will have to flow into a gas as it expands, to compensate for the work done in the expansion.

 6 **On the same axes, sketch and label curves of pressure against volume for:**
   a a fixed mass of gas;
   b twice the mass of the same gas at the same temperature;
   c the gas from part a at a higher and lower temperature.

7 **Repeat question 6 but plotting pressure against 1/volume.**

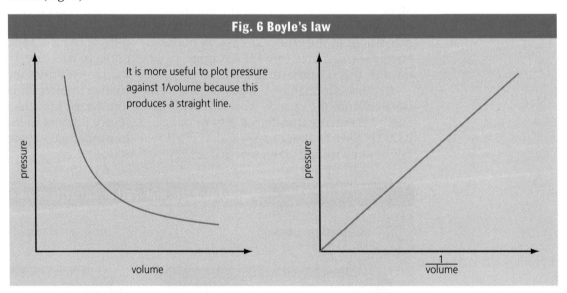

Fig. 6 Boyle's law

It is more useful to plot pressure against 1/volume because this produces a straight line.

pressure

volume

pressure

$\frac{1}{\text{volume}}$

Key ideas

 • An ideal gas expanding against a constant pressure must do work given by:

$W = p\Delta V.$

• For adiabatic expansion, $\Delta W = -\Delta U$.

• For isothermal expansion, $\Delta W = \Delta Q$.

10.4 How the fridge killed the cowboy

Water borne steam engines. The technology was developed before the science, but science made it possible to improve the technology.

Refrigeration defies the usual trend for energy to flow from a body at higher temperature to one at lower temperature. To 'pump' energy 'the wrong way' needs an input of energy from outside (Fig. 7). Work has to be done. The quiet hum of a fridge motor is work in progress.

The 'new' grasslands of the American West provided a vast area for growing food for the cities of the east. The food had horns and hooves, and beef enriched the diets of millions. The burger became a part of American heritage, and then spread through the world.

Live cows stay fresh, and they've got their own legs to walk on. But it took a lot of cowboys to lead a good sized herd to a distant railhead. As the rail network expanded, and new technology provided refrigerated trucks, the long distance work of the cowboy was over.

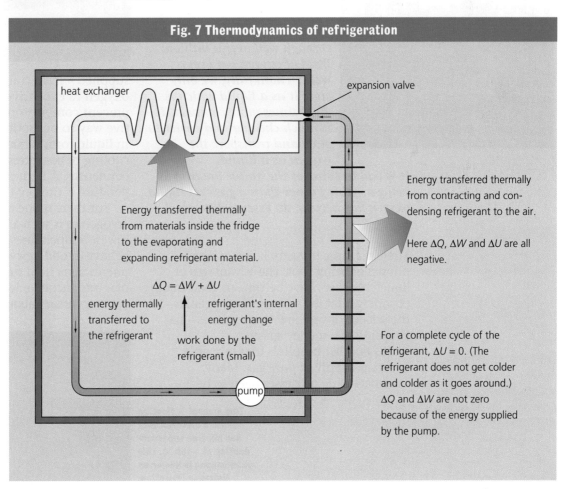

Fig. 7 Thermodynamics of refrigeration

heat exchanger

expansion valve

Energy transferred thermally from materials inside the fridge to the evaporating and expanding refrigerant material.

$$\Delta Q = \Delta W + \Delta U$$

energy thermally transferred to the refrigerant

refrigerant's internal energy change

work done by the refrigerant (small)

pump

Energy transferred thermally from contracting and condensing refrigerant to the air.

Here ΔQ, ΔW and ΔU are all negative.

For a complete cycle of the refrigerant, $\Delta U = 0$. (The refrigerant does not get colder and colder as it goes around.) ΔQ and ΔW are not zero because of the energy supplied by the pump.

Cold new world

If this airship was filled with oxygen gas instead of helium, it would only supply a typical hospital for a matter of minutes! This is far too little at too great a cost. It is far cheaper to store and transport oxygen as a liquid.

'Here at the hospital we get through well over a million litres of oxygen gas every week! Thankfully, we only store it as a liquid which is 2000 times more compact. It is much cheaper and easier to store and transport the oxygen as a liquid.

It is odd to think of the air we breathe as being anything other than a gas. Yet liquid oxygen has become an essential medical supply.'

There is a large industry based on the physics of being cool. The advantages of liquefying gases have become so great in our economy, that the science of **cryogenics** – the science of very low temperatures – has become a real money spinner.

It's not just hospitals that rely on a constant supply of pure gas. Many manufacturing processes need to be supplied – from common but essential oxygen to expensive inert gases that prevent combustion. The only cost effective way to transport gases from suppliers is in liquid form. This is usually done by cooling or compressing the gas until it condenses. A high pressure or a low temperature is the key to a cheap supply of gas.

But there is one more reason that cryogenics is such a hot topic. At the very lowest temperatures, materials start to behave in odd new ways. These strange phenomena hold the promise of entirely new and lucrative technologies that we can't yet even dream about.

This magnet is floating above a material that has become superconducting at −180 °C. This phenomenon is known as Meissner levitation.

11.1 Learning objectives

After working through this chapter, you should be able to:

- **explain** cooling by evaporation both in terms of latent heat and the particle model;

- **explain** why adiabatic expansion causes cooling;

- **describe** how the Joule–Kelvin effect is used to liquefy a gas, and describe the use of a countercurrent heat exchanger;

- **explain** why the Joule–Kelvin effect can cause heating as well as cooling;

- **describe** the changed properties of liquid helium at very low temperatures;

- **describe** the changed conducting properties of materials at low temperatures;

- **describe** existing and possible applications of superconductivity.

11.2 Nothing left to lose

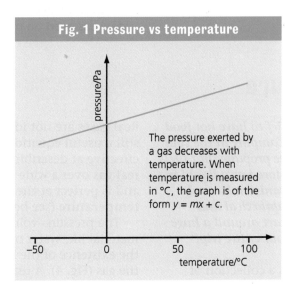

Fig. 1 Pressure vs temperature

pressure/Pa

The pressure exerted by a gas decreases with temperature. When temperature is measured in °C, the graph is of the form *y* = *mx* + *c*.

−50   0   50   100
temperature/°C

Fig. 2 Pressure vs temperature in kelvin

pressure/Pa

When temperature is measured in kelvin, K, the graph is of the form *y* = *kx*. This means that pressure is *proportional* to the absolute temperature (temperature in kelvin).

temperature/K

As a gas cools down, its particles lose energy. Could it go on losing energy, getting colder and colder? Surely not. There must come a point where the gas particles have no more internal energy left to lose – the gas is as cold as it can get. In practice it is impossible to extract energy from a material until it can lose no more, because energy always leaks back into the material from its warmer surroundings. However, the concept of an absolute minimum of internal energy, and an absolute minimum of temperature, is useful. We can base all measurement of temperature upon it, using the absolute zero of temperature as the starting point. The **absolute zero** of temperature is called zero kelvin, or 0 K.

Gas pressure and absolute zero

Moving particles of a gas exert pressure in a very simple way – they bump into things and bounce off them. A gas which has no internal energy left to lose has particles which are not moving, and so is unable to exert any pressure. Measurements of pressure exerted by gases at different temperatures confirm that pressure falls with temperature (Fig. 1). The relationship is of the form *y* = *mx* + *c*.

The graph does not pass through the origin, because 0 °C is just the temperature at which one substance, water, experiences a particular change of state. It has no significance beyond that. We would not expect gas particles to stop moving at the freezing point of water.

We can simplify the graph by moving the origin left to the point on the temperature axis where our straight line crosses it, by extending (or 'extrapolating') the line in that direction. Then the graph's origin is at the temperature at which the gas exerts zero pressure (assuming that it continues to behave in the same way as it gets colder and colder). If you do this for different masses of gas, or for different gases, the lines all cross the x-axis at the same temperature, which is roughly –273 °C. It seems that no gas can get any colder. It is the rock bottom of temperature – absolute zero.

1   **Why is it impossible, in practice, to produce and maintain a temperature of 0 K?**

2   **What is the link between zero pressure and absolute zero temperature?**

Key ideas

- The kelvin scale is defined in terms of the pressure exerted by a constant volume of an ideal gas.

- Absolute zero (0 K, –273.15 °C) is the temperature at which the particles of an ideal gas exert no pressure.

11.3   Under pressure

'It's a great relief to have hot food when you are camping in the cold or the rain. The propane that fuels our burner is stored as a liquid in a pressurised canister. It would certainly be impractical and dangerous to cart around a huge bag of gas for our entire trip!'

An **ideal gas** is a collection of completely independent particles. There are no forces between them, which means that the material cannot condense into liquid – it can only ever be a gas.

A graph of pressure against volume for a mass of ideal gas at a fixed temperature shows an inversely proportional relationship between pressure and volume. The gas obeys Boyle's law perfectly.

If pressure is inversely proportional to volume, then the product of pressure and volume is a constant:

$p \propto 1/V$

or, $p = \text{constant} \times 1/V$

$pV = \text{constant}$

Real gases are not ideal gases, but this is still a useful equation. The equation is effective at describing the behaviour of a real gas over a wide range of conditions and is perfect at the gas's **Boyle temperature** (see box).

The pressure–volume curves for a real material like water or carbon dioxide show the existence of the liquid state as well as the gas (Fig. 4). A real gas can, provided

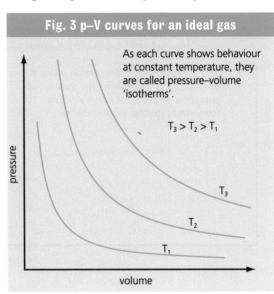

Fig. 3 p–V curves for an ideal gas

As each curve shows behaviour at constant temperature, they are called pressure–volume 'isotherms'.

$T_3 > T_2 > T_1$

T_3

T_2

T_1

pressure

volume

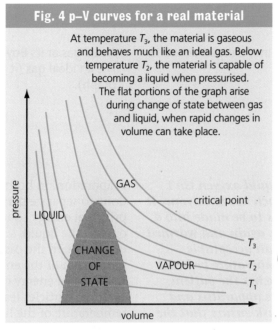

Fig. 4 p–V curves for a real material

At temperature T_3, the material is gaseous and behaves much like an ideal gas. Below temperature T_2, the material is capable of becoming a liquid when pressurised. The flat portions of the graph arise during change of state between gas and liquid, when rapid changes in volume can take place.

pressure

LIQUID

GAS

critical point

CHANGE
OF
STATE

VAPOUR

T_3

T_2

T_1

volume

that its temperature is not too high, be liquefied by putting it under pressure.

Notice in Fig. 4 that at higher temperatures (T_3) and pressures, the shape of the graph is similar to that of an ideal gas – the behaviour of the real gas approximates to that of an ideal gas. (This shows why the notion of an ideal gas is useful – it provides good predictions, some of the time, for the behaviour of real material.)

Notice also that above a certain temperature (T_2), the material can never be a liquid, only a gas. This is called the **critical temperature**. For carbon dioxide the critical temperature is 31 °C. Water has a much higher critical temperature of 647 °C. Above this temperature, water cannot exist as a liquid whatever the pressure – ice **sublimes** into steam.

Butane has a critical temperature of 152 °C, which means that it is possible to liquefy butane at normal everyday temperatures. This is very useful for transporting the material in liquid form, rather than transporting it as a gas.

Q 3 **Why does carbon dioxide turn directly from a solid into a gas (and vice versa) at normal temperatures and pressures?**

4 **The critical temperature of methane is 191 K. Why is methane not suitable for use in portable cylinders for camping stoves?**

The Boyle temperature

Graphs of pV against p show that pV is constant for an ideal gas. When pressure changes, volume changes to compensate exactly.

The pV versus p graphs for real gases (Fig. 6) are not the same as for the ideal gas (Fig. 5) for a number of reasons. For example, a small part of the volume of a real gas is taken up by the volume of the particles themselves. This volume becomes more significant at high pressures when the particles are close together.

At one particular temperature, the various factors that cause the behaviour of a real gas to differ from that of an ideal gas very nearly cancel out. Then the gas behaves almost exactly like an

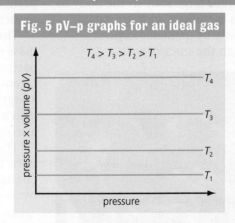

Fig. 5 pV–p graphs for an ideal gas

$T_4 > T_3 > T_2 > T_1$

pressure × volume (pV)

T_4

T_3

T_2

T_1

pressure

ideal gas – the pV against p graph is nearly a horizontal straight line. This temperature is called the Boyle temperature.

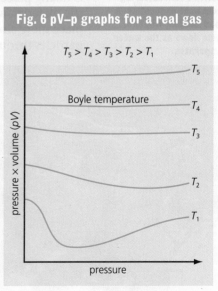

Fig. 6 pV–p graphs for a real gas

$T_5 > T_4 > T_3 > T_2 > T_1$

pressure × volume (pV)

T_5

Boyle temperature

T_4

T_3

T_2

T_1

pressure

- A real gas cannot turn into a liquid above its critical temperature.

- A real gas at its Boyle temperature behaves like an ideal gas (it has a straight pV versus p graph).

11.4 Cooling

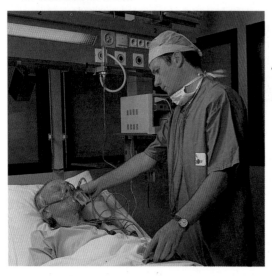

'Liquid oxygen isn't much use to anyone. It has to be made into a gas again and warmed to an acceptable temperature before it reaches the patient. The apparatus and mask ensure that the oxygen is released at a controlled level.'

Large crowds at outdoor festivals risk suffering from heat exhaustion. A good soaking will cool them down as the water evaporates.

Cooling by evaporation

In a liquid there are very significant forces between particles. The particles are not free of each other. It takes energy to separate them – to make the liquid vaporise. It doesn't matter whether the change of state is taking place on a large scale in the body of the material, as in boiling, or if it is taking place more slowly by gradual escape of particles through the surface, as in evaporation. In both cases, work must be done to separate particles. In boiling, the principal energy source is usually from outside the liquid, such as from the element of a kettle. In the case of evaporation, a large proportion of the energy can be taken from the internal energy of the liquid that the escaping particles leave behind. The temperature of the liquid falls if this energy is not replaced.

The fall in temperature due to evaporation can also be explained in terms of particle behaviour. In the body of a liquid, particles are closely packed but with a high level of freedom to move around. Each particle speeds up and slows down as it is tugged and pushed this way and that. The particles that are most likely to escape are the ones that happen to be moving quickly when they are near the surface. Their energy is above the average for the particles of the liquid as a whole. The reduction in the average kinetic energy of particles left in the liquid corresponds to a reduction in temperature.

The energy needed to vaporise a unit mass of material is a constant for any particular liquid, and is called its **specific latent heat of vaporisation**. To turn a kilogram of boiling water in a saucepan into a kilogram of steam takes a lot of energy: 2 261 000 joules.

The energy required to boil a specified mass of liquid at its boiling point without changing its temperature can be calculated by:

energy= mass × specific latent heat of vaporisation

$$\Delta E = m \times L$$

In the reverse process, condensation, the same amount of energy must be transferred

Table 1 Latent heat of vaporisation	
Material	Specific latent heat of vaporisation (J kg^{-1})
water	2 261 000
mercury	295 000
octane	292 000
tetrachloromethane	195 000
ethanol	839 000

out from the material. This is why steam can burn skin so badly: not only is the steam much hotter than your skin, the process of condensation makes a lot of energy available very quickly.

Cooling by adiabatic expansion

Any expanding gas, ideal or real, must do work to push something else out of the way – unless it is expanding into a vacuum. A real gas also needs an energy supply so that work can be done to pull particles apart, opposing the attractive forces between them. A gas expanding **adiabatically** (without thermally transferring energy to or from its surroundings) uses its own internal energy. So the temperature of the gas falls.

5 **Sweat emerges from pores at the same temperature as the lower layers of skin. Why does it cause cooling?**

6 **Explain, as fully as you can, why deodorant spray feels cool.**

The sudden expansion of CO_2 from a fire extinguisher is adiabatic. The CO_2 cools itself down, solidifying into a fog of dry ice particles.

Cooling a real gas

Just how good is the ideal gas as a model? How closely does it match real behaviour? Scientists in the mid-nineteenth century were interested in these questions, so that they could test the usefulness of the model. After all, there is no point in using a model that never provides good predictions of what actually happens.

They knew that an expanding ideal gas requires energy just to push other material out of the way. An ideal gas expanding into a vacuum would require no energy input at all (either from an external source or from its own internal energy) because there is no resistance to the expansion. A *real* gas expanding into a vacuum would still have to work against its own inter-particle forces. Real gases require an energy input. So a real gas expanding into a vacuum ought to take energy from itself (its internal energy) and from its surroundings. There ought to be a drop in temperature.

In 1853, James Joule and William Thomson (who later became Lord Kelvin) were the first experimenters to observe the predicted temperature drop. They passed gas through a tube, in which a porous plug separated one region of constant high pressure from a second region of constant low pressure (Fig. 7).

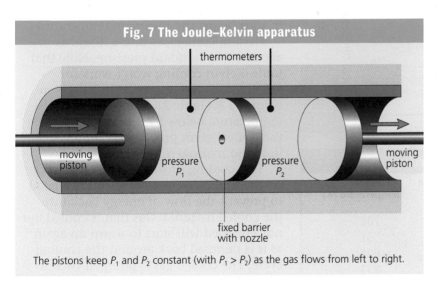

Fig. 7 The Joule–Kelvin apparatus

thermometers

moving piston

pressure P_1

pressure P_2

moving piston

fixed barrier with nozzle

The pistons keep P_1 and P_2 constant (with $P_1 > P_2$) as the gas flows from left to right.

As the gas expands from the high pressure to the low pressure region, it does not need to push other material out of the way – this work is done by the moving pistons at either end of the tube. So the only work done by the gas is that required to overcome its own inter-particle forces. The apparatus mimics expansion into a vacuum, and allows the expansion to continue for long enough for a temperature change to be detected.

By allowing the gas to flow for some time, and by keeping the apparatus well insulated, Joule and Kelvin were able to detect a temperature fall. They had found an important practical difference between a real gas and the ideal model. The fall in temperature of a real gas, resulting from expansion against its own attractive forces as it passes through a nozzle, is called the **Joule–Kelvin effect**. It is the most common method of cooling used to liquefy gases such as oxygen and helium.

7 Many scientists, before Joule and Kelvin, failed to observe the cooling of a gas expanding into a vacuum. What does that tell you about the closeness of the ideal gas model to the behaviour of a real gas?

Industrial considerations

The equipment that uses the Joule–Kelvin effect (Fig. 8), must do work on the gas to make it pass through the plug or nozzle. When you open the tap on a container of gas, the gas will not continue to emerge at the same pressure unless it is being pushed through. (This is exactly what the pistons in the Joule–Kelvin experiment did.) In other words, work is done on the gas to make it go through the nozzle. This means that the gas will warm up when the pressure drop is small (Fig. 9).

Above a certain temperature, called the **inversion temperature** of the material, the gas pressure is too high to let the gas do its own work. The work of pushing the gas into a lower pressure region will only cause heating. To cool a gas it is necessary to start below the inversion temperature.

Helium condenses into a liquid at about 4 K at standard pressure. Note that Joule–Kelvin cooling won't work for helium until the temperature has fallen below 51 K (Table 2). One way to get its temperature below 51 K before beginning the Joule–Kelvin process is to immerse it in liquid hydrogen.

This cooling process is obviously very costly, so the equipment is well insulated to prevent the flow of energy back into the cooled material. Gas that is cooled but not liquefied will start to warm up again as it is pumped back around the cooling cycle. The cooled gas is pumped back so that it is in close contact with the

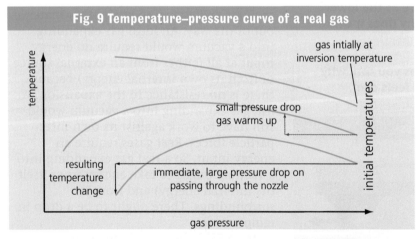

Fig. 8 Liquefying hydrogen

pre-cooling system to ensure gas is below its inversion temperature

counter-current heat exchanger

high pressure

low pressure

pump

expansion nozzle (Joule–Kelvin nozzle)

liquid hydrogen accumulating

Fig. 9 Temperature–pressure curve of a real gas

temperature

gas intially at inversion temperature

small pressure drop gas warms up

resulting temperature change

immediate, large pressure drop on passing through the nozzle

initial temperatures

gas pressure

Table 2 Properties of some materials			
Material	Boiling point at atmospheric pressure (K)	Critical temperature (K)	Inversion temperature (K)
hydrogen	20.4	33.2	205
helium	4.2	5.2	51
nitrogen	77.3	126	621
oxygen	90.2	154	893

incoming gas. This ensures that the incoming gas is cooled more. A **countercurrent heat exchanger** performs this task – usually through the use of concentric pipes, letting the cooler fluid flow around the warmer liquid (Fig. 8).

8 Why must hydrogen be pre-cooled before it can be liquefied by the Joule–Kelvin process?

9 Suggest some reasons why liquid nitrogen is much cheaper than liquid helium.

Key ideas

- Changing from liquid to gas requires a transfer of energy. Each kilogram of substance that changes state transfers an amount of energy that is characteristic of that material. This energy is called the specific latent heat of vaporisation.

- Evaporation and boiling require a transfer of energy to the material. Condensation requires a transfer of energy away from the material.

- Evaporation causes cooling by the removal of particles with larger than average internal energy.

- Adiabatic expansion cools a gas.

- Real gases that expand have to do work against the attractive intermolecular forces within the gas. This is known as the Joule–Kelvin effect.

- Forcing a gas to expand into a lower pressure will only produce cooling if the gas is below its inversion temperature.

11.5 Studying the supercool

'This is the sort of thing that makes one look twice and rub his eyes and wonder whether it is quite true... We looked around the building and finally found two nuclear physicists still at work. When they, too, saw the drops, we were happier.'
Kurt Mendelssohn who first discovered the phenomenon of 'film transfer'.

Just when everything about temperature and energy seemed to be understood, scientists got an unexpected shock.

Techniques of liquefying gases were becoming part of a new and prosperous industry, when researchers began to discover a variety of unexpected phenomena. These phenomena are now the focus of a great deal of cryogenic research. Large sums of money are lavished on this research because the potential rewards are enormous.

Helium's personality change
Helium turns to liquid at 4.2 K. Cool it a little further, to its 'lambda point', 2.17 K, and it starts to behave in a very odd way. The liquid flows with absolutely no resistance to motion. The liquid becomes perfectly slippery – it loses its viscosity. The phenomenon is called **superfluidity**, and it has very weird effects.

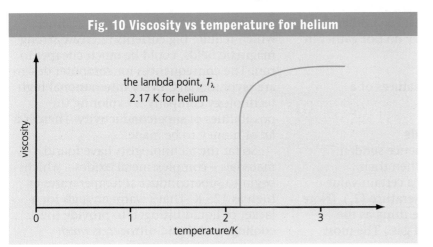

Fig. 10 Viscosity vs temperature for helium

the lambda point, T_λ
2.17 K for helium

viscosity

temperature/K

This beaker of superfluid helium drips every two or three seconds. The beaker isn't broken, a film of helium is climbing up and over the inside wall of the beaker at a rate of 30 cm s⁻¹!

The 'fountain effect'. A shaped tube immersed in helium at 1.2 K produces this 3 cm high spout.

significant change is the sudden loss of all electrical resistivity (Fig. 11). This is called **superconductivity**. A current, once started, will continue to flow endlessly around a superconducting circuit without the need for applied voltage – that is, without the need for an energy source.

In one of the first demonstrations of superconductivity, a current ran for more than two years without decreasing, and only stopped when the truck drivers refused to deliver any more liquid helium.

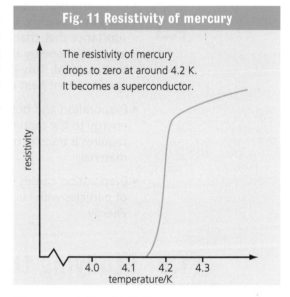

Fig. 11 Resistivity of mercury

The resistivity of mercury drops to zero at around 4.2 K. It becomes a superconductor.

The structure of $Y_2Ba_3Ca_2O_7$. Discovered in 1987, it superconducts near the temperature of liquid nitrogen.

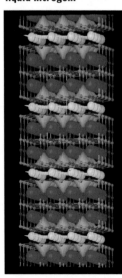

Superfluid liquid helium creeps up the sides of containers in a thin film. If you dip the bottom of an empty container into liquid helium, the liquid will flow up the outside walls and into the container until the levels are the same. This is called **film transfer**.

Liquid helium slowly boiling at temperatures of a few kelvin will suddenly stop bubbling when the temperature falls below the lambda point. The liquid may continue to turn into a gas, but particles can now move freely past each other to reach the surface, so they do not gather in bubbles.

10 What are the features of a superfluid?

Superconducting metals
Some metals also experience sudden changes in behaviour when their temperature falls below a certain value called the **critical temperature (T_c).** (Note that this is not the same thing as the critical temperature of a gas.) The most

The search for high T_c
If superconductivity happened at ordinary temperatures we could all have much cheaper electricity supplies because there would be no energy loss in transmission cables. Frictionless transport, far faster and needing less energy than conventional transport, would be possible using the levitation effect of magnets and superconductors. Medical body scanners, which require big currents to create strong magnetic fields, could be much cheaper to run. The consequences for computer design are revolutionary. Every international high technology company is exploring the possibilities of superconductivity. There is a *lot* of money to be made.

So far the technologists have found materials – complex metal oxides – which begin to superconduct at temperatures as high as 125 K. That's warm enough for a jacket of liquid nitrogen to provide the cooling, and liquid nitrogen is *much* cheaper than liquid helium. Many researchers are working on applications of the existing superconducting oxides, and others are working to find materials with still higher critical temperatures.

 11 What is 125 K in °C? Why are materials with critical temperatures of 100 K called 'high temperature' superconductors?

Table 3 Critical temperatures	
Material	T_c **(K)**
aluminium	1.20
gallium	1.08
tin	3.72
niobium/aluminium (Nb_3Al)	18.7
$YBa_2Cu_3O_7$	80
$Tl_2Ba_2Ca_2Cu_3O_{10}$	125

Superconductivity and electromagnetism

A magnetic field exists around any net flow of electric charge. The current in a superconductor is no exception, though superconductors do have some strange magnetic behaviour. A magnetic field cannot exist inside a superconductor, for example.

A problem occurs because strong magnetic fields can destroy superconductivity. So a superconductor's own magnetic field can be self-destructive. There is a maximum current density which a superconductor can sustain at a particular temperature. This imposes some limitations on the use of superconductors for generating strong magnetic fields, but strong fields are nevertheless possible – for levitation trains or for body scanners, for example.

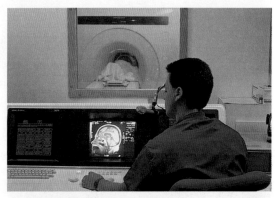

Magnetic resonance imaging (MRI) scanners use strong magnetic fields that are now provided by more efficient superconducting magnets.

This 'maglev' train is very economical with fuel because it feels no friction – powerful electromagnets levitate it above the track. With the advent of high temperature superconductors, which could sustain strong magnetic fields with very small electrical currents, this airport monorail could be the model for a future railway network.

Key ideas

- Helium condenses into a liquid at 4.2 K. Below 2.17 K, Helium loses all its viscosity and becomes superfluid.

- Many metals lose all their resistivity at very low temperatures to become superconducting.

- There is a large industry researching the possibilities of 'high temperature' superconductors.

Einstein's time

In this book, you have read about the many important changes in physics that have taken place in the last one hundred years. Perhaps the most baffling of these changes is discussed in this chapter: Einstein's theory of **Special Relativity**.

In 1905, Einstein wrote a revolutionary scientific paper. Although the paper was short, it suggested that scientists had to rethink *completely* their ideas of space and time. Einstein's theory suggested, amongst other things, that time flowed at different rates depending on how fast you were moving! The very idea that something as obviously constant as the flow of time could be stretched and squeezed in this way seemed unreal and unacceptable to many scientists.

Einstein was insistent. Time (*and* mass *and* distance), he said, could no longer be regarded as constant at all places to everyone. He had decided that it was the only way of explaining something that *was* truly constant – the speed of light.

The speed of light (2.998×10^8 m s^{-1}, 670 million miles per hour) is so fast that it is hard to relate it to everyday experience. This is only half the problem, because light does not even *behave* like anything else in everyday experience. Light is special.

The 'relativistic' stretching of time and distance is very real, but only noticeable at speeds approaching the speed of light. Anyone planning on travelling to distant stars will have to take this into account.

12.1 Learning objectives

After working through this chapter, you should be able to:

- **use** the concept of an inertial frame of reference;

- **explain** the significance of the invariance of the speed of light to our understanding of time;

- **describe** the role of the Michelson–Morley experiment in developing a scientific understanding of time;

- **calculate** the effects of time dilation, length contraction and relativistic mass change;

- **recall** the evidence for relativistic effects;

- **explain** why nothing can travel faster than light.

12.2 The speed of light

Albert Einstein turned physics on its head in 1905 when he outlined a theory in a paper entitled 'On the electrodynamics of moving bodies'. It was inspired by Einstein's firm conviction that the speed of light would always be measured as a constant 2.998×10^8 m s^{-1} *no matter how fast the measurer or light source was moving.*

James Clerk Maxwell had used ideas of electric and magnetic field to derive equations which not only predicted the existence of invisible electromagnetic radiations (like radio waves and X-rays), long before they were actually discovered, but had shown that the speed of light was related to other constants (see Chapter 8):

speed of light, $c = \dfrac{1}{\sqrt{\mu_0 \varepsilon_0}}$

μ_0 and ε_0 are constants associated with magnetic and electric fields. They are fundamental properties of space. Einstein picked up on Maxwell's formula and saw that it implied that the speed of light is also a fundamental property of space.

The aether

Before Einstein, electromagnetic waves were imagined to propagate (move) through a medium known as the **aether** (pronounced 'ether'). Physicists supposed that the constant speed of light predicted by Maxwell's equation was the speed at which light moved through the aether. The aether, whatever it was made of, existed throughout all of space. It had to be rigid enough to carry the rapid oscillations of light, yet thin enough to let massive planets move through it without any noticeable resistance.

Although the substance of the aether could not be detected, scientists suggested alternative ways of detecting its existence. They reasoned that if you were moving through the aether, you should observe aether waves (light) travelling at speeds slightly greater or less than Maxwell's value of 2.998×10^8 m s^{-1}. It seems like common sense that if something starts to move away from you, and you then follow after it, that the object will move away from you less quickly. This is certainly true of water waves (Fig. 1). The measured speed of a

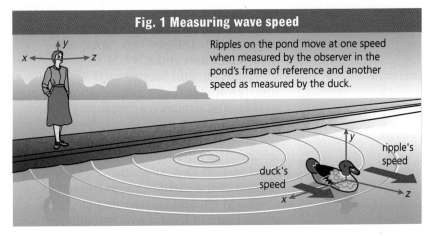

Fig. 1 Measuring wave speed

Ripples on the pond move at one speed when measured by the observer in the pond's frame of reference and another speed as measured by the duck.

duck's speed

ripple's speed

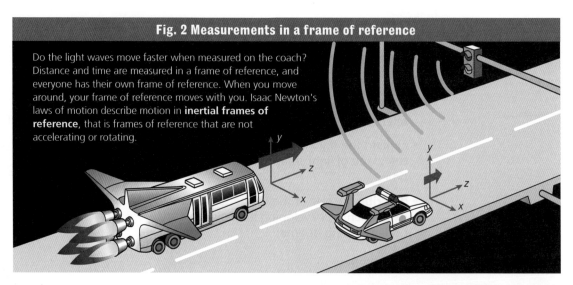

Fig. 2 Measurements in a frame of reference

Do the light waves move faster when measured on the coach? Distance and time are measured in a frame of reference, and everyone has their own frame of reference. When you move around, your frame of reference moves with you. Isaac Newton's laws of motion describe motion in **inertial frames of reference**, that is frames of reference that are not accelerating or rotating.

tennis ball depends on whether you are moving towards or away from the thrower with any speed. To find the 'real' speed of the ball, you must be in the 'proper' **frame of reference** (Fig. 2). The problem is then to decide which is *the* proper frame of reference.

Scientists started to think of the aether as the frame of reference in which all true measurements (such as the speed of light) could be made. They soon began to look for evidence of the motion of the Earth through the aether by measuring the speed of light as accurately as possible.

Fig. 3 The Earth moving through the aether

January

July

light from a   distant star

The Michelson–Morley experiment

Experiments became more and more sophisticated, but none of them was ever able to detect any change in the speed of light, no matter which direction the Earth was moving (Fig. 3). The experiment famous for decisively showing that the speed of light is measured to be constant no matter how the observer is moving was performed in 1887 by two Americans – A. A. Michelson and E. W. Morley.

Michelson and Morley used a Michelson **interferometer** (Fig. 4). Interferometers are outstanding devices for measuring distances – they can measure, for example, the growth of a plant from second to second. The Michelson interferometer was developed to look for evidence of the motion of the Earth through the aether.

The Michelson interferometer splits a single beam of light down two different

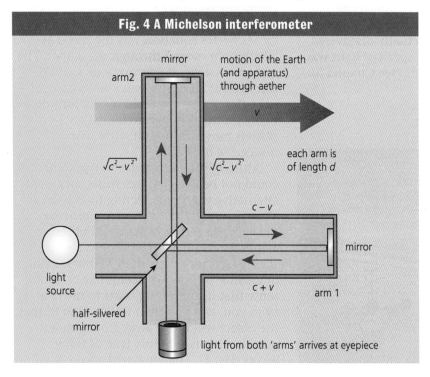

Fig. 4 A Michelson interferometer

mirror

arm2

motion of the Earth (and apparatus) through aether

v

$\sqrt{c^2 - v^2}$ $\sqrt{c^2 - v^2}$

each arm is of length d

$c - v$

mirror

$c + v$ arm 1

light source

half-silvered mirror

light from both 'arms' arrives at eyepiece

pathways that meet up at the end. If the pathways differ by a fraction of a wavelength, light from the two pathways is 'out of phase'. That is, the crests and troughs of the two sets of waves no longer coincide. The resulting interference pattern is seen in the eyepiece at the end of the apparatus.

Suppose that one of the mirror pathways (arm 1) is parallel to the motion of the Earth, which is moving at a speed v through the aether. Then, scientists expected, the speed of light going in one direction would be $c + v$, and in the other direction it would be $c - v$. The important point here is that the time taken to go from the half-silvered mirror to the end mirror and back again, depends on the speed of the apparatus through the aether. The resulting pattern of interference depends upon the difference in this time between the two pathways of the light.

If the light in arm 1 is travelling in the same direction as the aether, it has a speed relative to the apparatus of $c - v$ (upstream) and $c + v$ (downstream). The time to travel the length, d, of arm 1 and back is:

$$t_1 = \frac{d}{c - v} + \frac{d}{c + v}$$
$$= \frac{2dc}{c^2 - v^2}$$

The light in arm 2 (travelling at right angles to the motion through the aether) has a speed relative to the apparatus of $\sqrt{(c^2 - v^2)}$ in both directions (Fig. 5). The time to travel along arm 2 and back is:

$$t_2 = \frac{2d}{\sqrt{c^2 - v^2}}$$

If the apparatus is set up with one arm parallel to the motion through the aether, then there will be one fixed interference pattern seen in the eyepiece. If the whole apparatus is then turned so that the other arm is parallel to the motion through the aether, then the difference in time taken to cover the two pathways will change. The interference pattern will change.

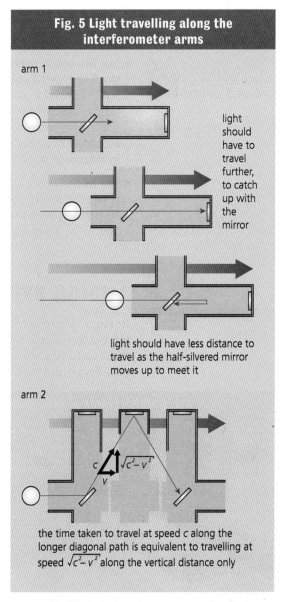

Fig. 5 Light travelling along the interferometer arms

arm 1

light should have to travel further, to catch up with the mirror

light should have less distance to travel as the half-silvered mirror moves up to meet it

arm 2

the time taken to travel at speed c along the longer diagonal path is equivalent to travelling at speed $\sqrt{c^2 - v^2}$ along the vertical distance only

Michelson and Morley tried this and nothing happened. It seemed as if the speed of light always stayed the same: never $c + v$, never $c - v$, only ever c. Physicists were reluctant to accept these findings, and other experimenters repeated this and similar experiments.

Many theories were proposed to solve the problem. Einstein's theory solved the problem by getting rid of the aether. He abandoned the quest for an absolute frame of reference, and declared that there could be no change in c no matter how much the observer moved.

Key ideas

- The Michelson interferometer measures small changes in distance (or time taken for light to travel that distance) by using the phenomenon of interference. A small change in distance (or time taken) results in a change of phase and a resulting change in interference pattern.

- The Michelson–Morley experiment produced a very useful negative result. It helped to prove that there is no stationary 'aether' – the medium through which light was imagined to propagate. Scientists had imagined that the aether was an absolute frame of reference.

- The speed of light is always measured as being constant, no matter how fast the measurer moves relative to the source of light.

- There is no such thing as absolute motion, all motion is *relative*.

12.3 Timing events

In Fig. 6, there are three inertial frames of reference – one for the car, one for the coach and one for the stationary police car, motorway and surrounding landscape.

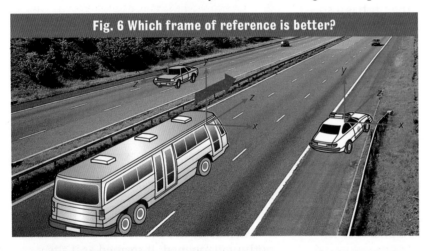

Fig. 6 Which frame of reference is better?

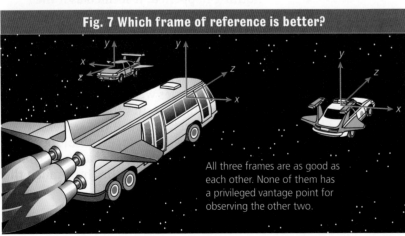

Fig. 7 Which frame of reference is better?

All three frames are as good as each other. None of them has a privileged vantage point for observing the other two.

Common sense says that the police car is in the frame of reference which is somehow superior – that it is the frame of reference from which objective observations can be made. Why do we say that? Probably because the police car is in a bigger frame of reference: the roadside and landscape. We assume that because it is bigger it is better. But Einstein decided that size doesn't matter.

Einstein took the negative result of the Michelson–Morley experiment to mean two things:

1 Physical laws are the same in all inertial frames of reference, so there is no such thing as an absolute frame of reference that is superior to all others (Fig. 7).

2 The speed of light is measured to be the same in all frames of reference.

These are sometimes called the postulates of relativity. Statement 1 says that nobody can say 'I am stationary, they are moving'. It is impossible to tell who is and is not moving – the (unaccelerated) motion is relative. Statement 2 says that no matter how fast you move towards or away from a source of light, you won't detect any change in the light's speed. Another observer in a different frame of reference, moving at a different speed to you, will also get the same value for the speed of light. Nothing else that we know behaves in this way – only light.

Imagine an interstellar coach that is being driven too fast (Fig. 7). A police officer fires a radar beam (electromagnetic waves) at the coach as it speeds away. The radar waves leave the police car at the speed of light (2.998×10^8 m s^{-1}). Common sense says that if you were to measure the speed of the radar waves from the speeding coach, the answer would be less than 2.998×10^8 m s^{-1}. But however carefully the coach passengers try to measure, and however fast the coach is going, they will always get the answer of 2.998×10^8 m s^{-1}.

The speed of light is the same in all frames of reference, *regardless* of the motion of the source or the observers. The consequences of this are unravelled over the next few pages.

1 a Standing on a railway platform, you drop a tennis ball. Describe the path of the ball. Describe what you see when you do the same on a train moving at constant velocity.

b Standing on the railway platform, you drop the tennis ball just as a train passes. Your twin on the train has just dropped a tennis ball too. Describe the path of your twin's tennis ball as you see it. Does your twin describe the path of your tennis ball in the same way?

2 An unruly passenger in the interstellar coach throws a ball at the police car! The ball's speed relative to the thrower is 90 km h^{-1}. Relative to the police car, the coach is speeding away at 70 km h^{-1}.

a If the passenger measured the speed of the ball in the coach's frame of reference, what would be the answer?

b If the police officer measured the speed of the ball, in the police car's frame of reference, what would be the answer?

3 Explain briefly why the coach passenger and the police officer would measure a different time for a burst of radar waves to travel from the police car to the coach.

About time

Our imaginary interstellar coach has a high-tech air-conditioning system with a laser that monitors air quality. A burst of laser light shoots up from a source in the floor of the coach, reflects off the coach ceiling, and returns to the laser source. The coach whizzes past another police car.

The coach passengers and the police officer observe the light travelling at the same speed. The path that the laser beam follows (from floor to ceiling and back) seems longer to the police officer than to the passengers (Fig. 8). This must mean that the observers get different results when they measure the *time* between emission and reception of the laser burst. Time is not the steady and reliable thing that we think it is. It is the speed of light in a vacuum that is steady and reliable, never changing.

The police officer measures a longer time for the event than the coach passengers. This phenomenon is called **time dilation**. Any event taking time t_0 in one frame of reference appears to take longer when observed from a second frame of reference moving at velocity v relative to the first frame. The exact time is given by:

$$t = \frac{t_0}{\sqrt{1 - \frac{v^2}{c^2}}}$$

Fig. 8 Travelling light

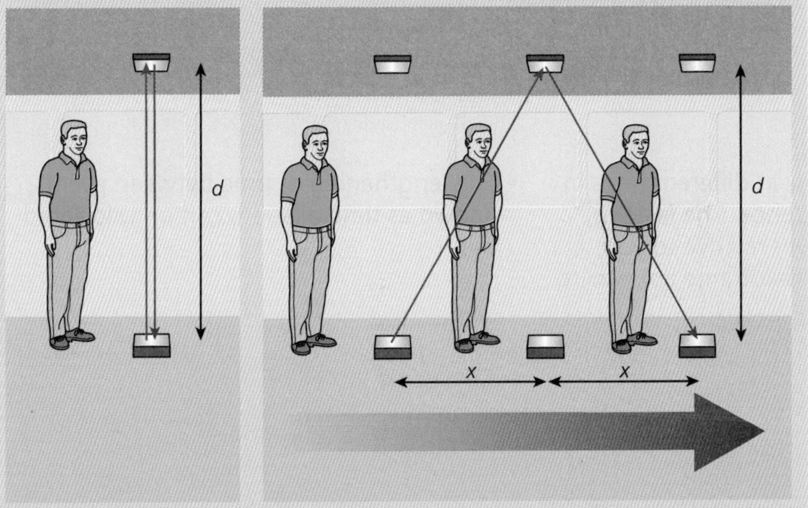

Passenger's view from inside the coach.

Police officer's view from outside the coach.

If v is a lot less than c, then there is not much difference between t and t_0. So in normal human events, we do not notice any relativistic time dilation. It only becomes significant as the value of v begins to approach the value of c.

Now imagine how the coach passengers see the police officer. Because the police car is travelling at a speed v relative to the coach, the passengers observe that time in the police car dilates in the same way! Time on the coach is stretched out for the police officer and time in the police car is stretched out for the coach passengers. The frames of reference are equivalent.

The time dilation formula

The time it takes for the laser burst to travel from floor to roof, according to the passenger, is:

$$\text{velocity} = \frac{\text{distance}}{\text{time}} \text{ or time} = \frac{\text{distance}}{\text{velocity}}$$

$$t_0 = \frac{d}{c}$$

The distance travelled by the laser burst, as seen by the police officer, is $\sqrt{(x^2 + d^2)}$, using the Pythagoras formula. This means that the time taken is:

$$\text{time} = \frac{\text{distance}}{\text{velocity}}$$

$$t = \frac{\sqrt{x^2 + d^2}}{c}$$

The value of x is the distance travelled along the motorway by the coach during the journey of the laser burst. The police officer measures x as equal to the coach velocity, v, times the time, t, for which he sees the laser pulse travelling upwards. The time taken for the journey of the laser burst, according to the observing police officer, is therefore:

$$t = \frac{\sqrt{(vt)^2 + d^2}}{c}$$

$$t^2 = \frac{v^2 t^2 + d^2}{c^2}$$

$$= \frac{v^2 t^2}{c^2} + \frac{d^2}{c^2}$$

But since $t_0 = d/c$:

$$t^2 = t^2 \left(\frac{v^2}{c^2}\right) + t_0^{\,2}$$

So, $t^2 \left(1 - \frac{v^2}{c^2}\right) = t_0^{\,2}$

$$t^2 = \frac{t_0^{\,2}}{\left(1 - \frac{v^2}{c^2}\right)}$$

$$t = \frac{t_0}{\sqrt{1 - \frac{v^2}{c^2}}}$$

Key ideas

- Time is observed to flow at different rates in different frames of reference. The faster a frame of reference moves relative to you, the longer an event in that frame appears to take.

- The lengthening of time between events, known as time dilation, can be calculated by:

$$t = \frac{t_0}{\sqrt{1 - \frac{v^2}{c^2}}}$$

12.4 Measuring distances

Relativity just (only just) makes an impact on speeds at the ordinary human scale. A very sensitive clock, carried at high speed to the Moon and back again, does not show the same time as an identical clock that remains on Earth. The Earth clock seems to have run faster because it records a longer time, as predicted by the time dilation formula.

It is with high speed sub-atomic particles that time dilation becomes more noticeable. Cosmic radiation arriving at the Earth's upper atmosphere causes an effect which can only be explained using relativistic ideas. The cosmic radiation interacts with the atmosphere, creating unstable particles called muons. Muons in laboratories, moving slowly, have lifetimes of 2.2 μs.

According to non-relativistic calculations, muons travelling at 99% of the speed of light, or 0.99 c, should be able to travel for just 600 metres in their 2.2 μs before ceasing to exist. But in fact the muons travel for about 4800 metres, and many of them get all the way from the upper atmosphere to the surface of the Earth.

Time dilation explains this mismatch.

The time dilation formula relates the measured time t to the time t_0 in the frame of reference of the measured body:

$$t = \frac{t_0}{\sqrt{1 - \frac{v^2}{c^2}}}$$

If $v = 0.99\ c$ then,

$$t = \frac{t_0}{\sqrt{1 - \frac{0.99^2 c^2}{c^2}}}$$

$$= \frac{t_0}{\sqrt{1 - 0.99^2}}$$

$$= \frac{t_0}{\sqrt{0.02}} = 7.07\,t_0$$

A fast muon's lifetime, measured by observers in Earth's frame of reference, is more than seven times longer than the lifetime measured in the muon's own frame of reference.

Of course, the muon is not moving at all in its own frame of reference – to the muon, it is the Earth and its frame of reference that is moving. Remember that although the Earth is big, its frame of reference is not superior to any other. The alternative way of looking at the situation, that the Earth is moving towards the muon at 99% of the speed of light is just as valid.

To the muon, its lifetime is just over 2 μs. To us, its lifetime is more than 14 μs. In the Earth's frame of reference the muon travels more than 7 times further than the muon travels in its own frame of reference. It is as if the muon measures a long distance in the Earth's frame of reference as being much shorter. This is another very real effect only noticed at high speeds.

This phenomenon of **length contraction** is complementary to time dilation. The length of an object travelling at a speed v is measured as:

$$l = l_0 \sqrt{1 - \frac{v^2}{c^2}}$$

where l_0 is the length of the object at rest or measured in its own frame of reference.

Fig. 9 Relativity in a television

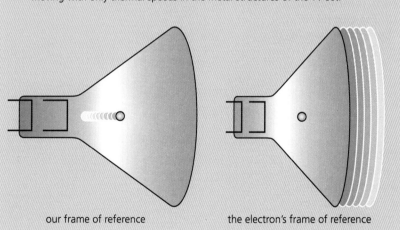

Electrons in an ordinary TV have speeds of about one-tenth that of light. Time passes more slowly for these high speed electrons than for electrons moving with only thermal speeds in the metal structures of the TV set.

our frame of reference   the electron's frame of reference

Length contraction

The length of our interstellar coach depends on the frame of reference you measure it in. Suppose that the coach's air-conditioning laser is mounted so that the beam travels horizontally, from the back of the coach to the front, where it is reflected. Again, the coach passenger and the police officer have different interpretations.

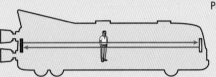

Fig. 10 How long is a coach?

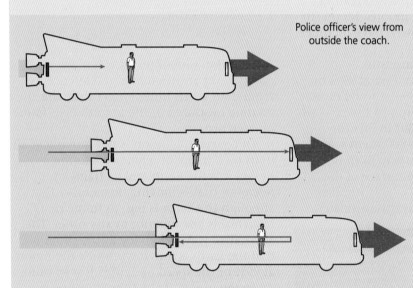

Passenger's view from inside the coach.

Police officer's view from outside the coach.

For the passenger on the coach, the length of the coach, is measured as L_0. The time taken for the journey of the laser burst to the front of the coach and back is given by:

$$\text{time} = \frac{\text{distance}}{\text{speed}}$$

$$t_0 = \frac{2L_0}{c}$$

For the police officer, the distance travelled by the laser beam to the front of the coach is equal to the length of the coach plus the extra distance due to the fact that the coach moves forward while the burst is travelling forward for a time t_1:

distance travelled by the laser burst = length of coach + distance travelled by coach

$$= L + vt_1$$

But we also know that, since the burst travels at the speed of light, the distance travelled by the laser burst = ct_1

so, $ct_1 = L + vt_1$

$$t_1 = \frac{L}{c - v}$$

The police officer sees the shorter return journey of the laser beam last for a time t_2:

$$ct_2 = L - vt_2$$

$$t_2 = \frac{L}{c + v}$$

The total time for the return journey as seen by the police officer is:

$$t = t_1 + t_2$$

$$= \frac{L}{c - v} + \frac{L}{c + v}$$

$$= \frac{L(c + v) + L(c - v)}{c^2 - v^2}$$

$$= \frac{2Lc}{c^2 - v^2}$$

The relationship between the time perceived by the police officer and the time for the same event as seen by a passenger travelling in the same frame of reference as the event is:

$$t = \frac{t_0}{\sqrt{1 - \frac{v^2}{c^2}}}$$

So, $$\frac{2Lc}{c^2 - v^2} = \frac{2L_0}{c\sqrt{1 - \frac{v^2}{c^2}}}$$

$$L = \frac{L_0\left(c^2 - v^2\right)}{c^2\sqrt{1 - \frac{v^2}{c^2}}}$$

$$= \frac{L_0}{\sqrt{1 - \frac{v^2}{c^2}}} \times \frac{c^2 - v^2}{c^2}$$

$$= \frac{L_0}{\sqrt{1 - \frac{v^2}{c^2}}} \times \left(1 - \frac{v^2}{c^2}\right)$$

$$L = L_0\sqrt{1 - \frac{v^2}{c^2}}$$

Q **4a** Estimate how long it would take for an electron, travelling at one-tenth of the speed of light, to travel from the electron gun to the screen in a television set (Fig. 9)?
  b What would be an electron's estimate of its journey time?
  c In the electron's frame of reference, the screen rushes towards it at one-tenth of the speed of light. How long is the distance from electron gun to screen from the electron's 'point of view'?

5 A coach is 12 m long according to its occupants. How long is it to a police officer, if the speed of the coach (relative to the police car) is:
  a 100 km h^{-1}?
  b 10^8 m s^{-1}?

6 The police officer reckons that the police car is 4 m long. What do the coach passengers think, at each of the same two speeds?

Key ideas

- Another relativistic effect observed at high velocities is that length (the separation between points in space) contracts. The length in the direction of movement of a fast moving object is measured as:

$$l = l_0 \sqrt{1 - \frac{v^2}{c^2}}$$

12.5 The universal speed limit

Suppose our coach on the interstellar motorway wants to avoid being caught for speeding. One option is to try to outrun the police car. This will require acceleration to a higher speed.

The coach's rocket engine can apply a continuous force, for as long as the fuel lasts. The police officer, observing the coach from an ever increasing distance and with ever increasing amazement, sees

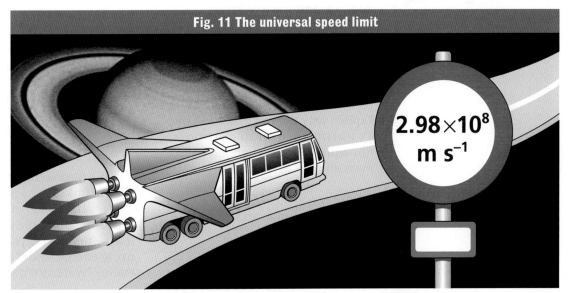

Fig. 11 The universal speed limit

2.98×10^8 m s^{-1}

a time dilation effect. The rocket engines are at full power, but the time taken to travel between the evenly spaced distance markers does not get much smaller. Though the coach's rocket engine is pushing with the same force, its acceleration is dwindling to zero.

Force, acceleration and mass are fundamentally linked by the familiar Newtonian equation, $F = ma$. Relativity does not challenge this formula – force is still equal to mass times acceleration. This means that a constant force with decreasing acceleration is only possible if mass is increasing. To the police officer, it seems that as the coach gets closer to the speed of light, its mass gets larger and larger. If it reaches the speed of light, there is no more acceleration. The coach seems to have infinite mass. It has reached the universal speed limit.

The change in apparent mass as a body approaches the speed of light follows a pattern which is similar to the time dilation pattern:

$$m = \frac{m_0}{\sqrt{1 - \frac{v^2}{c^2}}}$$

where m is the relativistic mass and m_0 is the rest mass – the mass of a body measured in its own inertial frame of reference.

7 The coach has a rest mass, m_0, of 5000 kg, and the maximum accelerating force that it can achieve is 10 kN. What is its maximum acceleration,
  a when travelling at 100 km h^{-1}?
  b when travelling at 10^8 m s^{-1}?

8 Explain why the force exerted by a TV electron gun on an electron is not equal to $m_0 a$, where m_0 is rest mass and a is acceleration.

Mass and energy

The difference between m and m_0 only becomes measurable when v is large. But if we observe a body that is approaching the speed of light, such as an electron in a TV tube or a proton in a synchrotron accelerator, then we observe an increase in its mass. Where does the mass come from? We already know that,

$$m = \frac{m_0}{\sqrt{1 - \frac{v^2}{c^2}}}$$

$$\text{or,} \quad m = m_0\left(1 - \frac{v^2}{c^2}\right)^{-\frac{1}{2}}$$

Expressions of the sort $(1 + x)^n$ can be rewritten using an approximation known as the **binomial expansion**. The binomial expansion, which was first worked out by Isaac Newton, says that to a good approximation,

$$(1 + x)^n \approx 1 + nx$$

when x is very small. (How it works can be left to the A-level mathematician.) This allows us to rewrite the relativistic mass formula rather differently:

$$m = m_0\left(1 - \frac{v^2}{c^2}\right)^{-\frac{1}{2}}$$
$$\approx m_0\left(1 + \frac{1}{2}\frac{v^2}{c^2}\right)$$
$$\approx m_0 + \frac{1}{2}m_0\frac{v^2}{c^2}$$
$$\text{So,} \quad mc^2 = m_0c^2 + \frac{1}{2}m_0v^2$$
$$\text{or,} \quad (m - m_0)c^2 = \frac{1}{2}m_0v^2$$

The change in mass $(m - m_0)$ is proportional to the kinetic energy of the body. The constant of proportionality is c^2. This means that if you try to increase your kinetic energy by accelerating, outside observers will measure this as an increase in mass. The amount of kinetic energy you gain, E, appears as an increase in mass, Δm, given by:

$\Delta mc^2 = E$ or (more famously) $E = \Delta mc^2$.

This means that mass and energy are closely linked. The principle of conservation of energy should really be called the principle of conservation of mass–energy. It is possible to create mass by using energy, and it is possible to create energy by destroying mass.

Key ideas

- The mass of a moving object increases as its velocity increases. An object can never accelerate to the speed of light because its mass becomes infinite at the speed of light. No amount of force can accelerate an object with infinite mass ($a = F/m$).

- The measured mass of a moving object is given by:

$$m = \frac{m_0}{\sqrt{1 - \frac{v^2}{c^2}}}$$

- Mass gained by accelerating to a high speed is directly related to the kinetic energy gained. Mass and energy are equivalent.

- $E = \Delta m c^2$

12.6 To be at the beginning again

At the end of the 20th century, many scientists were proclaiming that there was little left to do in the field of physics – just some tidying up. Of course, this had an eerily familiar ring to it, like a hundred year echo.

It was in the 1980s that scientists became really troubled by a problem known as 'non-linearity'. Physics had always been content to work on linear problems – problems that when multiplied by 10, the solution multiplied by 10 or some other predictable amount. Non-linear problems do not always have predictable solutions, and physics is now facing the fact that the real world is non-linear.

The non-linear way that particles and forces interact throws up whole new types of problems, problems that have given birth to new areas of scientific study. The equations of this new science describe the complexity and chaos of the world in ways that had previously eluded science because the calculations had been regarded as too 'ugly' to study. It is only the brute force of modern computers that has allowed us to open the door in to this strange new realm of knowledge.

'It makes me so happy. To be at the beginning again, knowing almost nothing. People were talking about the end of physics. Relativity and quantum looked as if they were going to clean out the whole problem between them. A theory of everything. But they only explained the very big and the very small. The universe, the elementary particles. The ordinary-sized stuff which is our lives, the things people write poetry about – clouds – daffodils – waterfalls – and what happens in a cup of coffee when the cream goes in – these things are full of mystery, as mysterious to us as the heavens were to the Greeks.

We're better at predicting events at the edge of the galaxy or inside the nucleus of an atom than whether it'll rain on auntie's garden party three Sunday's from now. Because the problem turns out to be different. We can't even predict the next drip from a dripping tap when it gets irregular. Each drip sets up the conditions for the next, the smallest variation blows prediction apart, and the weather is unpredictable the same way, will always be unpredictable. When you push the numbers through the computer you can see it on the screen. The future is disorder. A door like this has cracked open five or six times since we got up on our hind legs. It's the best possible time to be alive, when almost everything you thought you knew is wrong.'

From the play *Arcadia* by Tom Stoppard.

Data section

Units

Physicists usually use the International System of Units (Système Internationale, or SI). The base SI units that are most often used in physics are shown in Table 1.

Table 1 Base SI units

Quantity	Unit name	Symbol
length	metre	m
mass	kilogram	kg
time	second	s
electric current	ampere	A
temperature	kelvin	K
amount of substance	mole	mol

For convenience, any of the prefixes in Table 2 may be used with any unit: for example, the kilometre (1 km = 10^3 m) and the milliampere (1 mA = 10^{-3} A) are often useful.

Table 2 Prefixes for units

Prefix	Symbol	Meaning
tera	T	10^{12}
giga	G	10^9
mega	M	10^6
kilo	k	10^3
deci	d	10^{-1}
centi	c	10^{-2}
milli	m	10^{-3}
micro	μ	10^{-6}
nano	n	10^{-9}
pico	p	10^{-12}
femto	f	10^{-15}

Other units can be derived from the base units. For example, energy is normally measured in joules (symbol J), or multiples of joules (kJ, MJ), defined in terms of base units as kg m^2 s^{-2}. Some non-SI units can be converted to SI units as shown in Table 3.

Table 3 Unit conversions

Unit	Symbol	SI equivalent
atomic mass unit	u	1.661×10^{-27} kg
atmosphere	atm	101 325 Pa
degree Celsius	°C	1 K
litre	dm^3	10 m^3
electronvolt	eV	1.60×10^{-19} J

Formulae

Uniformly accelerated motion

$$v = \frac{\Delta s}{\Delta t}$$

$$a = \frac{\Delta v}{\Delta t}$$

$$v = u + at$$

$$s = \left(\frac{u + v}{2} \right) t$$

$$s = ut + \frac{at^2}{2}$$

$$v^2 = u^2 + 2as$$

$$p = mv$$

$$F = \frac{\Delta(mv)}{\Delta t}$$

$$F = ma$$

Circular motion

$$\omega = \frac{v}{r}$$

$$\omega = \frac{2\pi}{T}$$

$$a = \frac{v^2}{r} = r\omega^2$$

$$F = \frac{mv^2}{r} = mr\omega^2$$

Radioactivity and the nucleus

$$R = r_0 A^{\frac{1}{3}}$$

$$I = k\frac{I_0}{x^2}$$

$$\frac{\Delta N}{\Delta t} = -\lambda N$$

$$N = N_0 e^{-\lambda t}$$

$$T_{1/2} = \frac{\ln 2}{\lambda}$$

$$E = mc^2$$

Wave–particle duality

$$E = hf$$

$$hf = \phi + E_k$$

$$\lambda = \frac{h}{p}$$

$$\lambda = \frac{h}{\sqrt{2meV}}$$

$$R = \frac{0.61\lambda}{\sin\theta}$$

Thermodynamics

$$c = \frac{\Delta Q}{m\Delta T}$$

$$l = \frac{\Delta Q}{m}$$

$$\Delta Q = \Delta U + \Delta W$$

$$W = p\Delta V$$

Gases

$$pV = nRT$$

$$pV = \tfrac{1}{3}Nm\overline{c^2}$$

$$\tfrac{1}{2}m\overline{c^2} = \tfrac{3}{2}kT = \frac{3RT}{2N_A}$$

Electrons

$$F_{\text{magnetic}} = Bev$$

$$F_{\text{electric}} = \frac{eV}{d}$$

$$F_{\text{viscous}} = 6\pi\eta rv \quad \text{(Stokes' law)}$$

$$r = \frac{mv}{Be}$$

Relativity

$$c = \frac{1}{\sqrt{\mu_0\varepsilon_0}}$$

$$t = \frac{t_0}{\sqrt{1 - \frac{v^2}{c^2}}}$$

$$l = l_0\sqrt{1 - \frac{v^2}{c^2}}$$

$$m = \frac{m_0}{\sqrt{1 - \frac{v^2}{c^2}}}$$

Fundamental particles

Atomic particles

Particle	Symbol	Mass (kg)	Mass (u)
proton	p	$1.672\ 648 \times 10^{-27}$	1.007 276
neutron	n	$1.674\ 954 \times 10^{-27}$	1.008 665
electron	e^-	$0.910\ 953 \times 10^{-30}$	0.000 549

Sub-atomic particles

	Particle	Antiparticle	rest mass (MeV)	charge	baryon	lepton	strangeness
Nucleons							
proton	p	$\bar{p}$	938.3	+1	+1	0	0
neutron	n	$\bar{n}$	939.6	0	+1	0	0
Leptons							
photon	γ		0	0	0	0	0
electron	e^-	e^+	0.51	−1	0	+1	0
neutrino	ν	$\bar{\nu}$	0(?)	0	0	+1	0
Mesons							
pion	π^+	π^-	139.6	+1	0	0	0
	π^0		135.0	0	0	0	0
muon	μ^-	μ^+	105.7	0	0	+1	0
kaon	K^+	K^-	493.7	+1	0	0	+1
	K^0		497.7	0	0	0	+1
lambda	Λ^0		1115.6	0	+1	0	−1
sigma	Σ^+	Σ^-		+1	+1	0	−1

[Antiparticles have the opposite value to that shown]

Quark properties

Type	Baryon no.	Charge no.	Strangeness
u	$1/3$	$2/3$	0
d	$1/3$	$-1/3$	0
s	$1/3$	$-1/3$	−1
$\bar{u}$	$-1/3$	$-2/3$	0
$\bar{d}$	$-1/3$	$1/3$	0
$\bar{s}$	$-1/3$	$1/3$	+1

Constants

Constants

Quantity	Symbol	Value
speed of light	c	2.998×10^8 m s^{-1}
electron charge	e	1.602×10^{-19} C
electron rest mass	m_e	9.110×10^{-31} kg
proton rest mass	m_p	1.673×10^{-27} kg
neutron rest mass	m_n	1.675×10^{-27} kg
atomic mass unit	u	1.661×10^{-27} kg
specific charge	e/m	1.759×10^{11} C kg^{-1}
Planck's constant	h	6.626×10^{-34} J s
gravitational field strength (at Earth's surface)	g	9.807 m s^{-2}
gravitational constant	G	6.672×10^{-11} N m^2 kg^{-2}
permittivity of vacuum	ε_0	8.854×10^{-12} F m^{-1}
permeability of vacuum	μ_0	$4\pi \times 10^{-7}$ H m^{-1}
Avogadro constant	N_A	6.022×10^{23} mol^{-1}
Boltzmann constant	k	1.381×10^{-23} J K^{-1}
gas constant	R	8.314 J K^{-1} mol^{-1}
absolute zero		-273.15 °C

Common nuclides

Abundance given in 'relative terrestrial abundance'. This compares the abundance of each element with that of silicon. The abundance of silicon is set at 100.

Mass is given in atomic mass units, u. (1 u = 1.661×10^{-27} kg.) Half-lives given in minutes (m), hours (h), days (d) and years (a).

Common nuclides							
Name	Atomic no.	Abundance	Isotopes	Mass (u)	Half-life	Mode of decay	Isotope abundance (%)
carbon	12	0.14	9	9.031 039	0.13 s	β^+	
			10	10.016 860	19.4 s	β^+ and γ	
			11	11.011 430	20.4 m	β^+	
			12	12.000 000	stable		98.9
			13	13.003 355	stable		1.1
			14	14.003 241	5730 a	β^-	
			15	15.010 599	2,4 s	β^- and γ	
			16	16.014 701	0.74 s	β^- then n	
cobalt	27	0.01	60	59.933811	5.26 a	β^- and γ	
iron	26	22.0	54	53.939 612	stable		5.82
			55	54.938 296	2.6 a	e^- capture	
			56	55.934 939	stable		91.66
			57	56.935 396	stable		2.19
			58	57.933 277	stable		0.33
			59	58.934 877	45 d	β^-	
krypton	36	4.3×10^{-8}	80	79.916 380	stable		2.3
			81	80.910 590	2.1×10^5 a	e^- capture	
			82	81.913 482	stable		11.6
			83	82.914 135	stable		11.7
			84	83.911 507	stable		56.9
			85	84.912 531	10.7 a	β^- and γ	
			86	85.910 616	stable		17.3
			87	86.913 360	76.3 m	β^- and γ	
			88	87.914 453	2.84 h	β^- and γ	
			89	88.917 764	3.16 m	β^- and γ	
			90	89.919 520	33 s	β^- and γ	
lead	82	7.0×10^{-3}	203	202.973 365	2.2 d	e^- capture	
			208	207.976 66	stable		22.6
			214	213.999 84	26.8 m	β^- and γ	
manganese	25	0.3	55	54.938 0	stable		
nitrogen	7	9×10^{-12}	14	14.003 074	stable		99.6
oxygen	8	2.1×10^2	16	15.994 915	stable		99.7
			19	19.003 578	27 s	β^- and γ	
polonium	84	0.13	210		25.5 s	α and γ	
			212	211.988 865	3×10^{-7} s	α	
			216	216.001 92	0.145 s	α	

Name	Atomic no.	Abundance	Isotopes	Mass (u)	Half-life	Mode of decay	Isotope abundance (%)
protactinium	91	3.5×10^{-10}	234	234.043 42	1.17 m	β^- or γ	
radium	88	5.7×10^{-9}	224	224.020 20	3.64 d	α and γ	
			226	226.025 44	1622 a	α and γ	
			228	228.031 1	5.7 a	β^- and γ	
radon	86		220	220.011 39	55.5 s	α	
			222	222.017 61	3.82 d	α	
rubidium	37	0.14	85		stable		72.15
			87	86.908	4.7×10^{10} a	$\beta-$ and γ	27.85
			90	89.914 8	2.6 m	β^- and γ	
strontium	38	0.13	87	86.904	stable		7.02
			88	87.905 628	stable		82.56
			90	89.907 75	28.1 a	β^-	
thallium	81	1.3×10^{-3}	205		stable		70.5
			208	207.982 01	3.1 m	β^- and γ	
thorium	90	5.1×10^{-3}	228	228.028 73	1.91 a	α and γ	
			230	230.033 1	8×10^4 a	α or (α and γ)	
			232	232.038 08	1.4×10^{10} a	α or (α and γ)	100
			234	234.043 6	24.1 d	β^- and γ	
uranium	92	1.8×10^{-3}	233	233.039 65	1.6×10^5 a	α and γ	
			234	234.040 9	2.47×10^5 a	α and γ	
			235	235.043 94	7.13×10^8 a	α and γ	0.7
			236	236.045 59	2.39×10^7 a	α and γ	
			238	238.050 82	4.51×10^9 a	α and γ	99.3
			239	239.045 3	23.5 m	β^- and γ	

Answers to questions

Chapter 1

1
  a Kinetic energy.
  b Potential energy (electrostatic).
  c Around 2.5×10^{-13}, 250 fm.

2 The electrons have a kinetic energy of 125 GeV, so we can derive their momentum:

$$\tfrac{1}{2}mv^2 = 125 \times 10^9 \times e$$

$$v^2 = \frac{250 \times 10^9 \times e}{m}$$

$$v = \frac{\sqrt{250 \times 10^9 \times e}}{\sqrt{m}}$$

$$p = mv = \sqrt{250 \times 10^9 \times e \times m}$$

This gives us the wavelength of the electrons:

$$\lambda = \frac{h}{p} = \frac{h}{\sqrt{250 \times 10^9 \times e \times m}}$$

The first minimum in the diffraction pattern is at around 38°, so:

$$R = \frac{0.61\lambda}{\sin\theta} = \frac{0.61 \times \dfrac{h}{\sqrt{250 \times 10^9 \times e \times m}}}{\sin 38°}$$
$$= 3.4 \times 10^{-15} \text{ m, about 3.4 fm}$$

3 The 0, 0 data point should be used.
  $k \approx 1.8 \times 10^{-45}$ m³.

4 Taking $r = 0.134$ nm and mass of 197 u
  a 1.0×10^{-29} m³.
  b 197 u = 3.3×10^{-25} kg.
  c 33000 kg m⁻³.
  d The nucleus is very much smaller than the atom. Most of the atom is empty space, (nearly) all the mass is concentrated in the nucleus.

5
  a If you have a mass of 50 kg, this is all concentrated in the nuclei of your atoms with a density of 1.4×10^{18} kg m⁻³, in a volume:
$\rho = m/V$, so $V = m/\rho = 50/1.4 \times 10^{18} = 3.6 \times 10^{-17}$ m³.
Less than 4×10^{-11} cm³.
  b Empty space and electrons.

6 Strong nuclear force acts over a short distance, dropping considerably across the width of a ball of 200 nucleons, just over 10 fm.

7 Around 0.7 fm apart and infinitely far apart.

8
  a 0.7 fm
  b

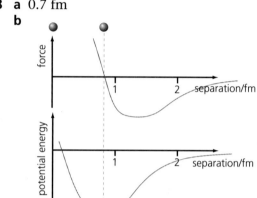

9 One of two things could happen, either the protons fly apart (repelled by the electrostatic force) or, if they are close enough, they may bind together (attracted by the nuclear force).

10 A million (10^6).

11 The forces in a nucleus are much stronger than in a water drop. The 'surface tension' or pull on a surface nucleon into the nucleus is that much greater.

Chapter 2

1 10 MeV, 1.6×10^{-12} J

2
  a 8 keV, 1.3×10^{-15} J
  b
$$\tfrac{1}{2}mv^2 = 1000 \times 1.3 \times 10^{-15}$$
$$v^2 = \frac{2.6 \times 10^{-12}}{1.673 \times 10^{-27}}$$
$$v = 1.2 \times 10^6 \text{ m s}^{-1}$$

  c
$$r = \frac{mv}{BQ} = \frac{1.673 \times 10^{-27} \times 1.2 \times 10^6}{0.8 \times 1.602 \times 10^{-19}}$$
$$= 0.016 \text{ m, 16 mm}$$

  d
$$t = \frac{x}{v} = \frac{\pi \times 0.016}{1.2 \times 10^6}$$
$$= 4.2 \times 10^{-8} \text{ s, 42 μs}$$

  e
$$f = \frac{1}{T} = \frac{1}{2 \times 4.2 \times 10^{-8}}$$
$$= 1.2 \times 10^7 \text{ Hz, 12 MHz}$$

3

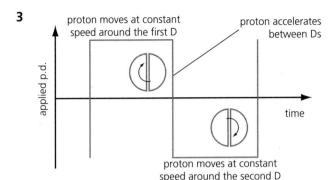

4 A large radius can achieve higher speeds for a given magnetic field strength. Can compensate for relativistic effects (mass change of high speed protons) by varying the magnetic field. Magnetic field does not have to cover the whole area of the circle. Acceleration can continue for longer, so higher speeds possible.

5 The particles need to be kept on a path of fixed radius. From $r = mv/BQ$, as v increases, B must increase to compensate. At very high speeds, approaching the speed of light, the mass of the particles starts to increase noticeably. Again, B must be increased to keep r constant.

6 a The gas in a simple ionisation chamber is of the usual density. This means that the ions do not accelerate enough before they collide with a gas particle. This contrasts with the low density gas in a GM tube which allows the high voltage to accelerate an ion through a long distance before colliding with a gas particle.

  b Ionising radiation can cause a high level of primary ionisation.

  c The detection of low intensity radiation.

Chapter 3

1 See Data section.

2 a
$$E = 2 \times m_e \times c^2$$
$$= 1.62 \times 10^{-13} \text{ J}$$

  b
$$E = hf, \text{ so } f = \frac{E}{h} = \frac{0.81 \times 10^{-13}}{6.626 \times 10^{-34}}$$
$$= 1.2 \times 10^{20} \text{ Hz}$$

  c $E = hf = 2 \times m_e \times c^2$

  so, $f = \dfrac{1.62 \times 10^{-13}}{6.626 \times 10^{-34}} = 2.4 \times 10^{20}$ Hz

  (twice the frequency of part b)

d Any surplus energy could be divided amongst the kinetic energy of the electron and positron.

3

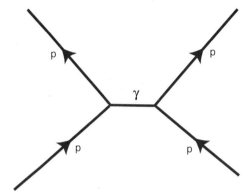

4 $\Delta E \times \Delta t < h$
$$mc^2 \times 10^{-23} < h$$
$$mc^2 < \frac{6.626 \times 10^{-34}}{10^{-23}}$$
$$m < 6.626 \times 10^{-11} \text{ J or 410 MeV}$$

5 See Data section.

6 a Charge not conserved.
  b Strangeness not conserved.
  c Baryon number not conserved.
  d Charge not conserved.

7 A baryon number of +1 and a strangeness of –1, means it must contain a strange quark. To get a charge of 0, there must also be an up and a down quark too. So a lambda particle contains: up, down and strange.

8 Baryons contain three quarks, mesons contain a quark and antiquark.

9 a is allowed. Quarks: $\overline{\text{D}}$U + UUD $\rightarrow$ $\overline{\text{S}}$U + UUS. The D and $\overline{\text{D}}$ collide and a S and $\overline{\text{S}}$ are created.

10 UDD $\rightarrow$ UUD. A down quark has 'flipped' to an up quark.

11 +1 $\rightarrow$ +1 –1 +1 allowed.
  0 $\rightarrow$ –1 +1 +1 not allowed.
  +1 $\rightarrow$ +1 –1 not allowed

Chapter 4

1 a $^{55}_{26}\text{Fe} + ^{0}_{-1}\text{e}^- \rightarrow ^{55}_{25}\text{Mn}$.

  b A neutral atom, as the atom has lost one proton and one electron, but only 'gained' a neutral neutron.

  c Mass of reactants = 54.938296. Mass of products = 54.9380. Mass defect = 0.0003 (to 1 sig. fig.). Q value = 0.0003 × 931.3 MeV = 0.3 MeV.

2 a $^{14}_{6}\text{C} \rightarrow ^{14}_{7}\text{N} + ^{0}_{-1}\text{e}^- + \bar{\nu}$

  b The nucleus loses a neutron but gains a positively charged proton, so the result is a positively charged ion.

  c Mass of reactants = 14.003 241.
  Mass of products = $(14.003\ 074 - m_\text{e}) + m_\text{e}$.
  Mass lost = 0.000 167.
  Q value = 0.000 167 × 931.3 MeV = 0.156 MeV.

3 Mass of reactants = 86.908
  Mass of products = $86.904 - m_\text{e} + m_\text{e}$
  Mass lost = 0.004 u × 931.3 MeV = 3.7 MeV
  $$\frac{\text{d}N}{\text{d}t} = -\lambda N \quad \lambda = \frac{\ln 2}{T_{\frac{1}{2}}} \quad N = \frac{10}{86.9} \times N_A \times 27.8\%$$
  $$\frac{\text{d}N}{\text{d}t} = -\frac{\ln 2}{4.7 \times 10^{10} \times 365 \times 24 \times 3600}$$
  $$\times \frac{10}{86.9} \times 6.02 \times 10^{23} \times 0.278$$
  $$= 9006$$

  9006 decays per second, power =
  $9006 \times 3.7 \times 10^6 \times 1.6 \times 10^{-19} = 5.3 \times 10^{-9}$ W.

4 Mass of He nucleus = $4.002\ 603 - 2m_\text{e}$. Binding energy = (mass of 2 protons + mass of 2 neutrons – mass of He nucleus) × 931.3 MeV. Binding energy = 0.030 377 × 931.3 MeV = 28.3 MeV.

5 $m_\text{e} = 0.000549$ u. Mass of Fe nucleus = $55.934\ 939 - 26\ m_\text{e} = 55.920\ 665$. Mass of 56 protons = 56.507 456. Mass defect = 0.586 791. Around 1.0% of the mass lost. If 1% of 1 kg is converted to energy: $E = mc^2 = 9 \times 10^{13}$ J.

(Now ask yourself: where do the neutrons come from?)

6 a Lead-208.
  Nuclear mass = $207.976\ 66 - 82m_\text{e} = 207.931\ 642$.
  Mass of nucleons = $82m_\text{p} + 126 \times m_\text{n} = 209.688422$.
  Mass defect = 1.75678 u.
  Lead-214.
  Nuclear mass = $213.999\ 84 - 82 \times m_\text{e} = 213.954\ 822$.
  Mass of nucleons = $82m_\text{p} + 132m_\text{n} = 215.740\ 412$.
  Mass defect = 1.785 59 u.

  b Lead-208. Binding energy per nucleon = 1.75678 × 931.3 MeV / 208 = 7.865 81 MeV
  Lead-214. Binding energy per nucleon =

1.785 59 × 931.3 MeV / 214 = 7.770 65 MeV

  c Lead-208 is more stable. This would be expected as it has more binding energy per nucleon.

7 a Polonium-214 is likely to be present only as a trace isotope.

  b
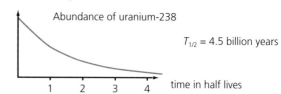
Abundance of uranium-238
$T_{1/2}$ = 4.5 billion years
time in half lives

8 a
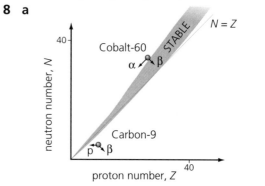

  b α heads towards a neutron rich zone. β moves in towards the zone of stability, so it is more likely.

  c Proton emission is more likely than β⁻, as it is a move towards the zone of stability.

Chapter 5

1 At 10 eV per ionisation, a 5 MeV particle will take 5 000 000/10 = 500 000 collisions before stopping.

2 a See Data section.

  b Alpha particles are over 7000 times more massive than beta particles and have twice the charge. This makes alpha particles slower and more likely to interact with other particles (strong ionising ability) so that their rate of loss of energy per unit distance travelled is much greater.

3 a $E = hf = 6.626 \times 10^{-34} \times 10^{18} = 6.626 \times 10^{-16}$ J
  $= 6.626 \times 10^{-16} \times 1.6 \times 10^{-19}$ eV
  $= 1.06 \times 10^{-33}$ eV

  b $E = \frac{1}{2}mv^2 = 6.626 \times 10^{-16}$ J
  $$v^2 = \frac{2 \times 6.626 \times 10^{-16}}{9.110 \times 10^{-31}}$$
  $$v = 3.8 \times 10^7 \text{ m s}^{-1}$$

  c Gamma radiation has a lot of energy but has no electrical charge. It is the strong electric field of alpha and beta radiation that gives them their ionising ability.

4 Alpha particles leave strong straight tracks because they are highly ionising (produces lots of ions which makes a strong track) and are much more massive than the electrons, so they are not deflected much in collisions. Beta particles are less ionising than alpha particles (a single charge produces a weaker field and induces less ionisation) and they are deflected through large angles when they collide with electrons in atoms. Gamma rays are very weakly ionising. When they collide with an electron they may be partially absorbed and the electron is liberated.

5 Food contains radiation! – This is very badly informed. It is likely that the writer means that food contains radioactive isotopes than radiation itself (which is always on the move). This is still a misunderstanding, because food contains *some* radioactive material as do all completely natural things.

Food contaminated by exposure to radiation! – Contaminated would seem to be the wrong word to use. Food is certainly *affected* by exposure to radiation. Alpha and beta radiation kills bacteria and small bugs on the food. The radiation also produces 'radiolytic products' in the food, which are identical to products caused by conventional cooking and preserving methods. The headline would be a worry if it specified neutron radiation, because this could induce unnatural levels of radioactivity in the food.

Food contaminated by traces of radioactive material! – A trace amount of radioactive material would only be natural. 12% of the 'background radiation' that a person receives in a year is from eating, drinking and breathing in the natural traces of radioactive material. This could be a serious worry if the writer means that the food has been contaminated by external or 'unnatural' sources of radiation, because ingestion of radioactive material can cause a severe amount of ionisation and damage to living cells.

6 a There are many candidates. The radionuclide should emit gamma radiation, beta radiation is acceptable, though alpha radiation is unacceptable on safety grounds. The half-life should be long enough for it last a reasonable length of time, plus it should decay into something harmless. Strontium–85 would fit this description.

b The best option would be to not use radioactive isotopes at all. Gamma, beta and X-radiation can all be generated mechanically – without radioactive sources.

7 a The intensity remains constant over very long distances.

b The intensity drops slowly in an exponential fashion – dropping in intensity by 50% over several hundred (or thousand) metres.

c The intensity drops quickly in an exponential fashion – dropping in intensity by 50% over only a few metres.

8 a

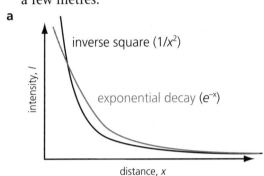

b A few cms of air has very little effect on gamma radiation.

c Close to a source, spreading is a much larger effect on intensity. The graph of $1/x^2$ changes much more rapidly than e^{-x} at small values.

9 Absorption of gamma radiation occurs randomly, such that the rate of absorption is proportional to the intensity of the radiation (resulting in an exponential decay). Absorption of an alpha particle is a gradual process, and all alpha particles with the same initial energy run out of energy after the same distance.

10 a

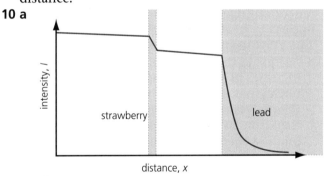

b From Table 3, μ of 0.4 MeV photon in lead is 2.57. $I = I_0 e^{-\mu x}$, so $0.001 = e^{-2.57x}$
By taking the natural logarithm of both sides of the equation:
$\ln 0.001 = -2.57 x$
so, $x = 2.7$ m.

11 Using $E = hf$ for each possible transition:

0.90 MeV → 0 MeV, 2.2×10^{20} Hz.

0.90 MeV → 0.28 MeV, 1.5×10^{20} Hz.

0.90 MeV → 0.66 MeV, 5.8×10^{19} Hz.

0.66 MeV → 0 MeV, 1.6×10^{20} Hz.

0.66 MeV → 0.28 MeV, 9.2×10^{19} Hz.

0.28 MeV → 0 MeV, 6.8×10^{19} Hz.

12 A beta decay liberates an amount of energy that is shared between three particles (the daughter nuclide, the beta particle and a neutrino). This sharing can leave the beta particle with any amount of energy between almost none and almost all (the other two particles will take some energy to conserve momentum).

13 a Well depth can be taken to be about 70 MeV (−40 to +30). The kinetic energy needed inside the nucleus to climb this potential is:

$$\tfrac{1}{2}mv^2 = 70 \times 10^6 \times e \text{ (in joules)}$$

$$v^2 = \frac{2.243 \times 10^{-11}}{4 \times 1.67 \times 10^{-27}}$$

$$v = 5.8 \times 10^7 \text{ m s}^{-1}$$

b If the alpha particle tunnels it only has to climb from −40 to around +15:

$$\tfrac{1}{2}mv^2 = 55 \times 10^6 \times e \text{ (in joules)}$$

$$v^2 = \frac{8.811 \times 10^{-12}}{4 \times 1.67 \times 10^{-27}}$$

$$v = 3.6 \times 10^7 \text{ m s}^{-1}$$

Chapter 6

1 A neutron triggers the fission by entering the nucleus to create an unstable nucleus of uranium-236. The fission releases free neutrons.

2 a As long as the binding energy per nucleon increases in a change, energy is released. Large nuclei split (fission) into nuclei lighter than themselves, and if the daughter nuclei are heavier than iron-56 this will produce an increase in binding energy per nucleon. Fusing small nuclei together into heavier nuclei will nearly always increase the binding energy per nucleon.

b Iron has the most stable nucleus – it has the most binding energy per nucleon. Fusing two iron nuclei together would produce a nucleus with less binding energy per nucleon. This requires an input of energy.

A young star is made up of light elements – hydrogen and helium – which it fuses together to release energy. As a star gets older it accumulates the products of fusion – heavier nuclei such as iron – and these may fuse if the conditions are right. This process takes energy and reduces the temperature of the star. The structure of the star – the balance between the outwards pressure of radiation and the inwards pull of gravity – changes.

3 a Alpha and gamma.

b The products of fission present in used fuel produce beta radiation. Neutrons will have transformed some nuclei to produce new radionuclides.

4 a $^{16}_{8}\text{O} + 3\,^{1}_{0}\text{n} \rightarrow {}^{19}_{8}\text{O}$.

b $^{19}_{8}\text{O} \rightarrow {}^{19}_{9}\text{F} + {}^{0}_{-1}\text{e}^- + \bar{\nu}$.

c Fluorine is enormously different from oxygen in its chemical behaviour. Oxygen atoms 'disappearing' from molecules in the concrete would cause the break down of the molecules and weaken the structure of the concrete.

5 a $10^4 \times 10^{12} = 10^{16}$ neutrons.

b From Fig.3 the binding energy per nucleon from mass number 235 to 120 increases by around 1 MeV, so a single fission event releases approximately 230 MeV.

This gives: 2.3×10^{18} MeV, or 370 kJ.

6 a Thermal neutrons have a kinetic energy comparable to that of particles their size in a hot gas.

b Uranium-235 absorbs thermal neutrons more easily than it absorbs fast neutrons.

7 The coolant in a PWR is water and this can become radioactive when exposed to a neutron flux. For that reason it is important that the primary cooling system is entirely contained. In a gas-cooled reactor, the primary cooling system can lead outside the shielding because the coolant nuclei (carbon and oxygen) do not absorb neutrons so much.

8 Advantages: Water acts as a moderator, so an extra moderator is not needed, which leads to a much more compact design. Water has a high specific heat capacity.

Disadvantages: The water can become radioactive. Water can liberate oxygen and hydrogen – both chemically reactive gases.

9 a The hydrogen will absorb neutrons to become deuterium.

b The absorption of neutrons by oxygen is a thousand times less frequent than that of hydrogen and it would take three neutrons (a billion times less frequent) to produce an unstable isotope of oxygen.

c H-3 (tritium) emits β.

10 a

momentum: $mv_1 = mv_2 + 12mv_3$

kinetic energy: $\frac{1}{2}mv_1{}^2 = \frac{1}{2}mv_2{}^2 + \frac{1}{2}12mv_3{}^2$

$$10^{10} = v_2{}^2 + 12v_3{}^2$$

so, $10^{10} = v_2{}^2 + 12\left(\dfrac{10^5 - v_2}{12}\right)^2$

$$10^{10} = v_2{}^2 + 12\left(\frac{10^{10} + v_2{}^2 - 2 \times 10^5 v_2}{144}\right)$$

$$12 \times 10^{10} = 12v_2{}^2 + 10^{10} + v_2{}^2 - 2 \times 10^5 v_2$$

$$0 = 13v_2{}^2 - 2 \times 10^5 v_2 - 11 \times 10^{10}$$

$$0 = \left(13v_2 + \left[11 \times 10^5\right]\right)\left(v_2 - 10^5\right)$$

$v_2 = {}^{-11}/_{13} \times 10^5 = 0.85 \times 10^5$ m s^{-1} backwards.

b Concentrating on the 'mean' neutron:

$$\frac{1}{2}m\overline{c^2} = \frac{3}{2}kT$$

$$\overline{c^2} = \frac{3kT}{m}$$

$$c = 1.98 \times 10^7 \text{ m s}^{-1}$$

11 a The coolant should not absorb neutrons at all for safety considerations. The moderator should preferably not absorb neutrons, but should interact with them significantly to absorb their energy. Control rods should strongly absorb neutrons.

b Boron or cadmium.

12 a 900 MW is 9×10^8 J per second. This corresponds to a mass loss of:

$$E = mc^2 = 9 \times 10^8$$

$$m = \frac{9 \times 10^8}{c^2} = 1.00 \times 10^{-8} \text{ kg, or } 10 \text{ }\mu\text{g}$$

10 μg per second.

b Energy inefficiency.

13 a

$$\frac{6.0 \times 10^{26}}{222} = 2.7 \times 10^{24} \text{ nuclei.}$$

b 2.7×10^{24} over $1\,000\,000 \times 1\,000\,000$ m², or 2.7×10^{12} nuclei per m².

c i)

$$\frac{dN}{dt} = -\lambda N$$

ii) $T_{\frac{1}{2}} = \dfrac{\ln 2}{\lambda}$ so, $\dfrac{dN}{dt} = -\dfrac{\ln 2}{T_{\frac{1}{2}}} N$

$$\frac{dN}{dt} = -\frac{\ln 2}{365 \times 24 \times 60 \times 60} N = 2.2 \times 10^{-8} N$$

d For a half-life of 100 hours,

$$\frac{dN}{dt} = -\frac{\ln 2}{100 \times 60 \times 60} N = -1.925 \times 10^{-6} N$$

i) $N = 0.001 \times 2.7 \times 10^{24}$, activity = 5.2×10^{15} Bq.

ii) $N = 0.001 \times 2.7 \times 10^{12}$, activity = 5.2×10^3 Bq.

iii) $N = 0.001 \times 1.35 \times 10^9$, activity = 2.6 Bq.

e The extra radiation represent a 13% increase of the natural background. This could be regarded as a tolerable increase, but isotopes (such as iodine-131) are taken up by the body from food and can result in a proportionally higher increase in exposure.

Chapter 7

1 Vacuum pump technology which relied on electro-magnetic motors.

2 See page 72.

3 a $\dfrac{e}{m} = \dfrac{1.60 \times 10^{-19}}{1.67 \times 10^{-27}} = 9.58 \times 10^7$ C kg^{-1}

b $\dfrac{e}{m} = 9.58 \times 10^7 \times \dfrac{2}{4} = 4.79 \times 10^7$ C kg^{-1}

c 0

d $\dfrac{e}{m} = 9.58 \times 10^7 \times \dfrac{79}{197} = 3.84 \times 10^7$ C kg^{-1}

4 $r = \dfrac{mv}{Be}$ and $v = \dfrac{V}{dB} = \dfrac{10^4}{B}$

$$r = \frac{m \times 10^4}{B^2 e}$$

$$B = \sqrt{\frac{10^5}{e/m}} = 7.5 \times 10^{-4} \text{ tesla}$$

5 Millikan uses the word atom to refer to discrete particles in general. The word is now used in a technical sense to refer to the specific discrete particle that is the smallest particle of an element.

Chapter 8

1 a

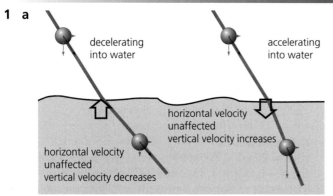

decelerating into water

accelerating into water

horizontal velocity unaffected
vertical velocity increases

horizontal velocity unaffected
vertical velocity decreases

b Light, when it slows down, refracts towards the normal. The diagram shows that particles slowing down refract away from the normal.

2 a See pages 81 and 82.

b Huygens' wave theory explained propagation, reflection and refraction, but could not explain colour or polarisation. Newton's particle theory explained propagation, reflection, refraction, colour and polarisation. Apparatus would not be able to show the interference of the very small wavelength waves until later in the century. The speed of light in water could not be measured until the next century. (See page 83.)

c Newton's prestige in the scientific community and the existence of his powerful theories that were based on forces and particles helped to persuade people that light was made of particles. You could also argue that it is easier to imagine light as a stream of particles than as a wave.

3 a As the Earth moves away from an event, the light from the end of the event has to 'catch up' and travel a little bit further than the light from the beginning of the event travelled. This is why the event appears to last longer.

b An event that takes time t_0 that appears to take time t_1 as you approach it (at speed v) and time t_2 as you run away from it. The difference between the measured time and t_0 is due to the Earth traversing a distance x given by vt_0:

$$t_1 = t_0 - \frac{x}{c} \text{ and } t_2 = t_0 + \frac{x}{c} \text{ and } x = vt_0$$

$$t_2 - t_1 = \frac{2vt_0}{c}$$

$$\frac{v}{c} = \frac{t_2 - t_1}{2t_0}$$

If we assume that t_0 is the average of t_2 and t_1 then:

$$\frac{v}{c} = \frac{t_2 - t_1}{t_2 + t_1}$$

So you can measure c as accurately as you know v and can measure the small time difference $t_2 - t_1$.

4 $$t = \frac{x}{v} = \frac{68000}{2.98 \times 10^8}$$

$$\text{rps} = \frac{1}{8} \div \frac{68000}{2.98 \times 10^8} = \frac{2.98 \times 10^8}{8 \times 68000} = 547.8$$

5 Hertz confirmed the existence of previously unknown phenomena that were predicted by Maxwell's work. This sort of confirmation is liable to increase people's confidence in a theory, leading to the theory being accepted as probably true.

6 The key difference is the temperature. The electric heater is the coldest, it peaks in intensity in the infrared. The intensity quickly drops off through the visible spectrum, so that red is more intense than the blue end. An electric lamp is hotter, peaking in intensity in the yellow region of the visible spectrum, which is why it is bright but contains more yellow than a pure white mix. The hot welding lamp peaks in intensity in the ultraviolet. The intensity is even across the visible spectrum, but rather larger at the blue end.

Chapter 9

1 Optical microscopes are only able to resolve objects down to around 10^{-7} m in size. This is good enough to resolve individual cells and bacteria, both very important in the understanding and advancement of medicine. It is not enough to resolve atoms ($\approx 10^{-10}$ m) or molecules ($\approx 10^{-9}$ m) though it was enough to observe Brownian motion – the first indirect evidence for the existence of tiny, constantly moving, discrete particles.

2 $$\lambda = \frac{h}{p} = \frac{6.6 \times 10^{-34}}{9.110 \times 10^{-31} \times 10^7}$$
$$= 7.24 \times 10^{-11} \text{ m}$$

3 a $$\lambda = \frac{h}{p} = \frac{6.6 \times 10^{-34}}{9.110 \times 10^{-31} \times 10^6}$$
$$= 7.24 \times 10^{-10} \text{ m}$$

b $$\lambda = \frac{h}{\sqrt{2me \times 1000}}$$
$$= 3.88 \times 10^{-11} \text{ m}$$

4

$$10^{-9} = \frac{h}{\sqrt{2meV}}$$

$$2meV = \left(h \times 10^9\right)^2$$

$$V = \frac{h^2 \times 10^{18}}{2me} = 1.5 \text{ volts}$$

Chapter 10

1 a Yes (most probably).
  b No (unless the heater is set at body temperature).
  c No (most probably).
2 a There is a flow of energy to the water because the water is colder.
  b The energy is shared out over a larger mass of water. Temperature is related to the amount of internal energy and the mass of the material.
3 Yes. Work ($\Delta W = \Delta Q - \Delta U$) could also come from lowering the internal energy of the steam which could include the latent heat of vaporisation, released when the water condenses back into water.
4 a The formula $W = p\Delta V$ assumes that there are no intermolecular forces in the gas. These forces are present in real gases, though they are very small compared to the large forces of air pressure, so the equation is still very useful.
  b If the real gas was under high pressure, the particles would be close enough for the forces between them to be significant.
5 The expansion is adiabatic at first because the expansion is so fast that no energy could be transferred – this is why the first blast of air can be so cold. As the pressure starts to equalise, the expansion is much slower, and the air stops cooling itself down and ends up expanding isothermally.

6

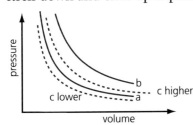

7

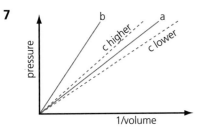

Chapter 11

1 If something was at 0 K, its surroundings could only be warmer, so there would be a flow of energy into the colder region which would warm it up.
2 Absolute zero is the point at which an ideal gas exerts zero pressure.
3 The critical temperature of carbon dioxide is much lower than ordinary room temperatures.
4 Methane is not suitable for use in portable cylinders because it cannot be compressed into a liquid at ordinary temperatures. Its critical temperature is –82 °C (191 K). This would mean having to refrigerate the cylinder all the time.
5 Sweat is able to evaporate, which means that thermal energy leaves the skin as internal energy of evaporating particles of sweat. This leaves the body with less internal energy and a lower temperature.
6 Deodorant spray feels cool because it emerges from the can propelled by a gas that expands adiabatically. The adiabatic expansion produces a cooling effect. (The expanding gas could also encourage evaporation which would also produce a cooling effect.)
7 The Joule–Kelvin effect must be very small to have gone unobserved for so long. This must mean that the effects of the intermolecular forces are hard to detect and that real gases are very close to being 'ideal' gases.
8 Hydrogen has to be pre-cooled because its inversion temperature is 205 K, well below room temperature. Any attempt to cool it by a Joule–Kelvin process would fail above this temperature.
9 Liquid nitrogen has an inversion temperature way above room temperature (621 K), so it does not need to be pre-cooled before liquefaction. Helium, on the other hand, can not be liquefied before it has been cooled all the way down to 51 K (perhaps with liquid hydrogen which also has to be pre-cooled before it can be liquefied).
10 See pages 113 and 114.
11 125 K = –148 °C. This is cool, but still not as cool as relatively cheap liquid nitrogen (77.3 K).

Chapter 12

1 a On the railway platform, the ball drops vertically, speeding up as it falls. On a train at constant velocity, the path appears identical.

b The twin's ball describes a simple parabola as it drops vertically at an accelerated velocity and moves horizonatally at a constant velocity. The twin should describe your tennis ball in exactly the same way (though travelling in the opposite direction).

2 a 90 km h^{-1}.

b 90 – 70 = 20 km h^{-1}.

c The key point to understand here is that both the coach passenger and the police officer see the waves moving at the same speed: 3×10^8 m s^{-1}. One way to think about this is to consider the distance that the waves have to traverse.

The coach passenger sees the waves having to travel the distance between the police car and coach at the point of firing, but the police officer see the waves having to catch up to the receding coach. Different distances covered at the same speed must mean that the events happen in different amounts of time.

4 a Speed of 2.998×10^8 m s^{-1}, distance of 0.3 m,
$$t = \frac{x}{v} = \frac{0.3}{2.998 \times 10^8} = 10^{-9} \text{ m s}^{-1}, \text{ a nanosecond.}$$

b With v/c about 0.1,
$$t = \frac{t_0}{\sqrt{1 - 0.1^2}} = 1.005 t_0.$$

c $l = l_0 \sqrt{1 - 0.1^2} = 0.995 l_0.$

5 a
$$l = l_0 \sqrt{1 - \left(\frac{100 \times \frac{1000}{3600}}{2.998 \times 10^8}\right)^2} = l_0, \text{ still 12 m.}$$

b
$$l = l_0 \sqrt{1 - \left(\frac{10^8}{2.998 \times 10^8}\right)^2} = 0.942 l_0 = 11.3 \text{ m.}$$

6 a 4m

b $0.942 \times 4 = 3.8$ m.
The coach passengers observe exactly the same contractions (100% and 94%) that the police officer would observe of the coach.

7 a At 100 km h^{-1}, there is no need for a relativistic caclulation, so: $a = F/m = 2$ m s^{-2}.

b $F = ma$ or $a = \dfrac{F}{m} = \dfrac{F\sqrt{1 - \dfrac{v^2}{c^2}}}{m_0}$

$$a = \frac{10000}{5000} \sqrt{1 - \left(\frac{10^8}{2.998 \times 10^8}\right)^2}$$
$$= 2 \times 0.942 = 1.88 \text{ m s}^{-2}.$$

8 Relative to the electron gun, the electron ends up speeding off at 1/10 of the speed of light. This is fast enough for relativistic effects to be noticeable. The average mass of the rapidly accelerating electron as 'measured' by the electron gun is larger than m_0, so the force exerted by the electron gun is larger than $m_0 a$.

Glossary

absolute zero The lowest possible temperature: all molecular motion stops at absolute zero.

absorbed dose The energy absorbed from ionising radiation in joules per kilogram. Absorbed dose is measured in grays (Gy).

absorption spectrum Radiation emitted by a source can be selectively absorbed by a material between the source and the observer, e.g. absorption of a star's light by clouds of interstellar gas. This can produce a series of dark lines or bands that are characteristic of the absorber.

activity The number of decays (or emissions) per second in a radioactive source (measured in becquerel, Bq).

adiabatic A gas expands adiabatically when there is no energy transfer into or out of the gas (ΔQ is zero). The gas must take energy from its own internal energy to expand($\Delta W = -\Delta U$), which results in a change in its temperature.

aether (Pronounced 'ether'.) The medium that was imagined to carry waves of electromagnetic energy.

alpha particles Strongly ionising, short range radiation emitted by some radioisotopes. An alpha particle is two neutrons and two protons tightly bound together.

atomic mass units 1 atomic mass unit = 1 u = 1/12 of the mass of an atom of carbon-12. This is close to the mass of a single proton or neutron.

antiparticles a particle identical in mass to another more common particle, but different in other properties, e.g.. charge, baryon number and strangeness. A bar over the particle letter, e.g. p, indicates that it is an antiparticle.

attenuation coefficient The constant μ in the equation of attenuation of gamma radiation:

$$I = I_0 \times e^{-\mu x}$$

The coefficient depends on the medium that the gamma radiation is passing through and the energy of the gamma photons. The larger the value, the faster the intensity drops.

avalanche effect Causes a single ionising particle to produce the strongest possible avalanche of ionisation. In a Geiger–Müller tube, the applied voltage and the gas pressure are set so that a single ionisation event accelerates the ion and free electrons so that they collide with, and ionise, other atoms, which in turn collide with, and ionise, further atoms.

baryon a particle, a kind of hadron, with baryon number of +1.

baryon number a number assigned to an observable particle which is the result of a combination of particular quarks. Baryons all have baryon number of +1, and their antiparticles have baryon number of –1.

beta particles High speed electrons emitted from the nucleus of some radioisotopes.

binding energy The total binding energy of a nucleus is the energy required to completely separate all of its nucleons.

binomial expansion The binomial expansion states that to a good approximation,

$$(1 + x)^n \approx 1 + nx$$

when x is very small. The full expansion contains $n + 1$ terms consisting of a coefficient and a power of x. In this approximation only the first power is considered, because all further powers (x^2, x^3 and so on up to x^n) are considered to be vanishingly small if x is already small.

black-body radiation A black body is a perfect absorber of (heat) radiation. Black bodies are also the best possible emitters. A black body absorbs all of the radiation that falls upon it and reflects none. The temperature of a black body determines the amount of radiation that it emits at each wavelength.

Boyle temperature The temperature at which a real gas behaves the most like an ideal gas (when pressure multiplied by volume is almost constant).

chromatic aberration An optical defect in lenses that causes light of different wavelengths to be focused at different focal points.

conservation rules Constraints on the type of particle interactions that are possible. Only some types of decays and interactions between particles are observed. Many possible interactions are never seen. One constraint appears to be that charge remains the same before and after any interaction. There are two further such conservation rules, of properties called baryon number and strangeness.

countercurrent heat exchanger A device used in liquefaction that minimises heat gain by keeping the cooled outgoing gas in close contact with the gas that is to be cooled.

critical mass An uncontrolled chain reaction can occur in a body of fissionable material such as enriched uranium provided that enough neutrons collide with fissionable nuclei. If the body of material is too small, below the critical mass for a sphere, too many neutrons escape from the material without inducing fission.

critical temperature (gas) The temperature above which a gas can not be compressed into a liquid.

critical temperature (superconductor) The temperature below which a metal loses all its resistivity and becomes superconducting.

cryogenics Branch of physics concerned with the production of very low temperatures and associated phenomenon.

cyclotron The cyclotron is a small flat cylindrical can, split into halves called Ds. Charged particles such as protons are accelerated by potential difference between the Ds and made to travel in near-circular motion by a magnetic field. The increasing speed of the charged particles causes them to spiral outwards. The potential difference alternates so that the particles always experience accelerating force when moving between the Ds.

daughter nucleus Fission produces a small number of free neutrons and two nuclei which are slightly less than half of the size of the initial or parent nucleus. These are the daughter nuclei.

de Broglie relationship Particles, such as electrons, can display wave wave behaviour. Their wavelength, λ, a wave property, depends on their momentum, p, a particle property, as described by de Broglie's relationship:

$$\lambda = \frac{h}{p} \quad \text{or} \quad p = \frac{h}{\lambda}$$

decay chain Many nuclides decay into nuclides which are also radioactive. There may be a series or chain of decays before a stable nuclide results.

dose equivalent A way of quantifying the effect on the human body of ionising radiation, measured in sieverts:
dose equivalent (sieverts) =
absorbed dose (grays) × weighting factor
The weighting factor ranges from 20, for very harmful alpha radiation, down to 1, for gamma and beta radiation.

diffraction The spreading out of the edges of waves to occupy areas which would otherwise be in 'shadow'.

down quark A fundamental particle, constituent of protons and neutrons.

electric field strength At any point in an electric field, this is the force per unit charge on a tiny test charge placed at that point.

electronvolt The kinetic energy transferred to a particle with the charge of an electron when it is accelerated through a potential difference of one volt. One eV is 1.6×10^{-19} J.

exchange particles the forces between particles, such as electric force and the strong nuclear force, can be explained in terms of other particles moving between them. These are the exchange particles. The exchange particle for the electric force, for example, is the photon.

film transfer The process by which superfluid liquid helium moves up the sides of a container in a thin film. If you dip the bottom of an empty container into liquid helium, the liquid will flow up the outside walls into the container.

frame of reference Every body exists in a frame of reference. The body and its frame of reference always move together, and share the same time-scale. An inertial frame of reference is one that is not accelerating.

fundamental particle Constituents of all matter. These include quarks (make up protons, neutrons, etc.), leptons (these include electrons and neutrinos) and bosons.

Feynman diagrams A representation of the exchange of particles in an interaction.

fission Fission is the splitting of a large nucleus to create two smaller ones and a few, typically three, free neutrons.

fusion If two small nuclei can overcome their electrical repulsion then they may join to make a larger nucleus. As with fission of large nuclei this results in an increase in binding energy per nucleon and thus a net energy release.

gamma radiation Penetrating, short-wavelength ionising radiation emitted by some radioisotopes.

graviton The exchange particle that is supposed to carry the gravitational force. There is no evidence for the existence of gravitons.

gray The unit of absorbed dose, equivalent to one joule absorbed per kilogram.

hadron Particle composed of quarks. Hadrons include the baryons (like neutrons and protons) and mesons (like pions and kaons).

ideal gas An imaginary model of a gas in which there are no attractive forces and in which the particles have no volume.

interference The result of wave combination. The displacement of two or more interfering waves is summed together. If two waves are in phase they produce constructive interference.

interferometer An interferometer is an instrument, as used by Michelson and Morley, which uses interference phenomena to measure the speed of light.

inversion temperature The temperature above which the process of pushing a gas into a lower pressure region can only ever cause heating. A gas must be cooled to its inversion temperature before it can be cooled further using the Joule–Kelvin effect.

isothermal At constant temperature. Constant temperature means constant internal energy ($\Delta U = 0$). For a gas to expand isothermally, there must be a supply of energy to the gas to match the work being done ($\Delta W = \Delta Q$).

Joule–Kelvin effect The change in temperature of a gas forced to expand through a small hole or porous material. Work is done by the gas to overcome its own inter-particle forces, so its internal energy drops.

kaons A kind of meson.

length contraction The 'proper' length of a body is a measurement made within its own frame of reference. A measurement made from a different frame of reference, relative to which the body is moving, gives a reduced result, as given by:

$$l = l_0 \sqrt{1 - \frac{v^2}{c^2}}$$

lepton the lepton family of particles include the electron and the neutrino. They are fundamental particles, with no internal structure. They take part in weak interactions but do not feel the strong force.

linear accelerator (linac for short) An accelerator consisting of a line of tubes positioned end to end. Charged particles are accelerated by the alternating potential difference applied to the tubes.

mass defect, mass difference Every nucleus has a smaller mass than the total mass of its constituent nucleons, hence a mass difference.

mesons Particles made up of a quark and an antiquark.

moderator The material, often graphite or water, used in a nuclear reactor to slow down neutrons.

nucleons Neutrons and protons.

pair production In a pair production event a photon's energy is manifested as the masses of an electron and a positron.

parent nucleus An unstable nucleus that decays to produce a daughter nucleus.

photoelectric effect The emission of electrons from a metal surface caused by light of sufficiently high frequency.

photons Quanta of electromagnetic radiation. They carry an amount of energy, E, that depends upon the frequency of the radiation. $E = hf$, where h is Planck's constant.

pions Type of meson that can act as an exchange particle between neutrons and protons at very short range (a few fm).

positron The antiparticle of an electron.

Q value The energy liberated during a nuclear transformation.

quantum (plural, quanta) This can refer to the smallest quantity of some property (such as energy) or to a discrete particle that carries that quantity.

quantum mechanics The highly successful branch of physics that describes the behaviour of fundamental particles in terms of the exchange of quanta.

quantum tunnelling A phenomenon that allows events to occur that were once considered energetically impossible. Alpha particle emission from a nucleus is much more common than would be expected if the particles had to gain enough energy to get over the potential barrier of the nucleus. It is as if the particles can tunnel through potential barriers to other energetically allowable areas.

quarks Fundamental particles which, in combination, make up all particles called hadrons. Three types of quark are of interest in considering the structure of protons, neutrons and pions. These are called the up, U, down, D, and the strange, S, quarks. (The three other quarks are: charm, top and bottom)

resolving Distinguishing between separate parts of an image in an optical instrument.

rest mass The mass of a body in its own frame of reference, in which it is at rest. As an object's speed approaches the speed of light its effective mass, as defined by the fundamental equation $F = ma$, increases, as given by:

$$m = \frac{m_0}{\sqrt{1 - \frac{v^2}{c^2}}}$$

semiconductor A substance that has an electrical conductivity between that of an insulator and conductor, which also increases with temperature.

sievert The unit of dose equivalent.

Special Relativity Einstein's theory concerning observers in relative uniform (unaccelerated) motion and the principle that the laws of physics (and specifically the speed of light) are always the same to all observers.

specific latent heat of vaporisation The energy needed to vaporise a unit mass of material at a constant temperature.

Stokes' law Named after Sir George Stokes (1819–1903). The viscous, or drag, force of a medium on a sphere moving through it can be calculated as:

$$F_{\text{viscous}} = 6\pi\eta r v$$

where v is velocity, r is the sphere's radius and η is the medium's coefficient of viscosity.

strange quark A fundamental particle.

strangeness Property of some quarks and hence of some hadrons. The need to conserve strangeness is a rule that particle interactions follow. This explains why many interactions which would otherwise be seen do not happen.

strong nuclear force (interaction) The force holding nucleons together is neither gravitational nor electrical force but a third force which acts only at very short range, but within that range is strong.

superconductivity The phenomenon of a material losing all of its resistivity, allowing an electric current to flow continually without the need of an applied voltage. This usually occurs at very low temperatures (a few kelvin above absolute zero), though 'high-temperature' superconductors have been discovered recently.

synchrotron A synchrotron is an accelerator in which particles gain energy as they travel in a circular [or near circular] path of constant radius.

terminal velocity The final unaccelerated velocity that an object reaches when falling due to gravity through a resistive medium. Terminal velocity is reached when the viscous, or drag, force of the medium exactly balances the weight of an object (the force due to gravity).

thermodynamics The study of the movement of heat through systems.

threshold frequency The minimum frequency of light that induces the spontaneous emission of electrons in a metal by the photoelectric effect. Light below this frequency has no effect on the metal, even at a high intensity.

time dilation Time does not pass at the same rate in frames of reference which are in relative motion. This is a consequence of the fact that the speed of light is the same in the different frames of reference. Time passing in the same frame of reference as a body is denoted t_0, while the time for the same event measured from a different frame of reference is denoted t. Their relationship is given by:

$$t = \frac{t_0}{\sqrt{1 - \frac{v^2}{c^2}}}$$

ultraviolet catastrophe The conflict of wave theory with the observations of black-body radiation. The theory predicted that small wavelengths should be accompanied by a large intensity. Only low intensities are observed. The cause of this low intensity was impossible to explain using a wave model of light.

up quark A fundamental particle constituent of protons and neutrons.

wave–particle duality The term used to describe the fact that light behaves as a wave and a particle. Subatomic particles, such as electrons, show wave and particle properties.

weak interaction Many particles change into other particles by processes that cannot be explained by the strong force, gravity or electromagnetism. The short range influence responsible for such changes (or decays) is the weak interaction. Beta decay is an example of a particle change governed by the weak interaction.

work function The energy needed to remove an electron from a material in thermionic or photoelectric emission processes.

Biographical glossary

Al-Haytham (c.965–c.1038)

Born at Basra (now in modern Iraq). Work in optics influential in West until 17th century.

Al-Haytham rejected the ancient Greek theory that light was emitted by the eye and reflected off the object viewed. He constructed the first known camera obscura and worked on the idea that rainbows were generated in the atmosphere by refraction.

Anderson, Carl (1905–1991)

Born in New York, USA. Discovered the positron and the muon. Awarded Nobel prize for physics in 1936.

Anderson worked at the California Institute of Technology to produce better cloud chamber detectors, which led to his discovery of antimatter.

Becquerel, Antoine Henri (1852–1908)

Born in Paris, France. Discovered radioactivity almost by accident. Shared the Nobel prize for physics with Pierre and Marie Curie in 1903.

Becquerel was studying fluorescence and X-rays when he happened to leave a sealed bag of uranium salts (which were known to fluoresce) on top of a photographic plate in a drawer for a few days. On developing the plate, Becquerel discovered marks in the place that the salts had been lying. This led Becquerel to investigate the properties of the penetrating radiation given off by the uranium.

Bohr, Niels (1885–1962)

Born in Copenhagen, Denmark. Formulated the quantum theory of electronic structure in atoms and of spectral lines.

Worked with Ernest Rutherford on the nuclear model of the atom. The orbiting electrons in this model were unstable because they should continually radiate light and lose energy as they accelerate around the nucleus. To stop the electrons spiralling into the nucleus, Bohr suggested that electrons could only occupy certain orbits, because their (angular) momentum could only change in jumps.

In 1943 he fled from the Nazis by boat to Sweden and then by aircraft to England. Bohr had been working on the fission of uranium and made contributions to the atomic bomb development at Los Alamos in the USA. He helped found CERN and was outspoken on the problems of nuclear power.

da Vinci, Leonardo (1452–1519)

Born at Vinci, near Florence, Italy. Inventor, painter and anatomist.

Leonardo's scientific investigations were many and various. He invented many instruments for measuring and was very interested in designing flying machines. His many beautiful illustrations of anatomy include bones, musculature, the heart and the fetus.

de Broglie, Louis (1892–1987)

Born at Dieppe, France. Pioneered the study of the wave mechanics of particles.

Louis was heir to an illustrious family but was drawn to study physics by his elder brother, Maurice. His 1924 doctoral thesis extended wave–particle duality to all matter. Wave–particle duality had first been proposed by Albert Einstein in relation to light only. When the wave nature of matter was demonstrated in 1927 it only took another two years before he was awarded the Nobel prize.

Dirac, Paul Adrian Maurice (1902–1984)

Born in Bristol, England. Founder of quantum mechanics, formulated the relativistic wave-equation for the electron.

His relativistic wave-equation accurately described the energy levels of the hydrogen atom, but it also correctly predicted that electrons have 'spin' (and accurately described the associated magnetic effect) and the existence of 'negative energy states' that were later described as antimatter. Awarded the Nobel prize in 1933, jointly with Schrödinger.

Einstein, Albert (1879–1955)

Born at Ulm, Württemberg, Germany.

In 1901, Einstein, then living in Switzerland, left school in the hope of becoming a teacher. He was unable to get a post because he was a Jew, and he eventually found a job as an office junior in the Berne Patent Office. In 1905, Einstein published three remarkable papers: the first on quantifying Brownian motion for the direct proof of the existence of molecules; the second on the quantum behaviour of light; and the third outlined his special theory of relativity.

In 1915, Einstein set out his more comprehensive general theory of relativity which was concerned with accelerated motion and gravity. Einstein's fame was such that when the predictions of his theory were confirmed, it made front page news around the world.

Though Einstein's contribution to physics was enormous, he was only awarded the Nobel prize for his work on the quantum behaviour of light and the photoelectric effect.

Faraday, Michael (1791–1867)

Born at Newington, Surrey, England. Invented the dynamo and discovered benzene.

Michael Faraday, son of a blacksmith, had a rudimentary education and became a bookbinder's apprentice at the age of 14. He read many of the books that came to be re-bound, and one day discovered a copy of the *Encyclopaedia Britannica*. The article on electricity fascinated him, but entrance to the scientific world was no easy matter for him. By chance he was recommended to Sir Humphry Davy by one of the bookbinder's customers. Davy had been temporarily blinded by an experiment and needed someone to write down his notes and take dictation.

Faraday started off as a chemist, but quickly turned to the study of electric and magnetic phenomena. He made important discoveries in electrolysis and went on to develop the concepts of fields of force. Faraday also made a huge contribution to the public understanding of science by starting up public lectures and producing educational and entertaining lectures for children.

Feynman, Richard (1918–1988)

Born in New York City, USA. Theoretical physicist, invented Feynman diagrams.

Feynman was a popular lecturer, renowned for his practical jokes. Feynman's greatest achievement in physics was the theory of quantum electrodynamics that combined quantum mechanics, electromagnetism and special relativity. He worked on the Manhattan Project to develop the atomic bomb and was critical of NASA's failure to prevent the *Challenger* disaster.

Geiger, Hans (1882–1945)

Born at Neustadt, Rhein-Pfalz, Germany. Pioneer of nuclear physics and inventor of the Geiger counter.

After working with Ernest Rutherford on the nature of alpha particles, Geiger went on to demonstrate the scattering of alpha particles from gold foil with his colleague E. Marsden. This discovery prompted Rutherford to formulate his nuclear model of the atom.

Hooke, Robert (1635–1703)

Born at Freshwater, Isle of Wight, England. One of the most brilliant scientists of 17th century England.

Hooke started his scientific career as assistant to Robert Boyle. He later became first the curator and then secretary of the Royal Society. 'Mister' Hooke did not achieve equal recognition with his contemporaries at the Royal society, which included Sir Isaac Newton, though he is now acknowledged to have been a very creative and inventive scientist.

He designed and built many instruments including a demonstration of the improved resolving power of glass lenses over the naked eye. He also put forward many theories ahead of their time: in 1672, he suggested that light was a wave with transverse properties; in 1674, he suggested that planetary motion was based on an inverse squared force from the Sun and the linear momentum of the planets. Hooke also studied the phenomena now known as Newton's Rings in great depth.

Hooke had many arguments with other scientists (including Newton and Huygens) over questions of priority, saying that he had already made the discoveries claimed by others. Hooke's law, the law relating force and extension in an elastic material, was first published by him as an anagram in Latin to establish his prior claim to that discovery.

Joule, James (1818–1889)

Born at Salford, England. Established the mechanical theory of heat.

In 1843, Joule first estimated the equivalence of mechanical work and 'thermal' energy. He reported that '838 ft lb. of work' raised the temperature of '1 lb. of water by 1 °F'. The unit of work, and energy, is named after him in honour of this work.

Kelvin, Lord *see* Thomson, William

Kepler, Johannes (1571–1630)

Born at Weil, Württemberg, Germany. Famous for his laws of planetary motion.

Kepler's scientific ideas were often based on his own mystical ideas about the universe, which derived in part from his protestant beliefs. He speculated that the orbits of planets were perfectly mathematically arranged in some manner, and developed the idea that each planet's orbit was on a sphere that was surrounded by one of the regular solids (cube, dodecahedron, etc.) which was in turn surrounded by the next planet's sphere, and so on.

Newton, Sir Isaac (1642–1727)

Born at Woolsthorp, Lincolnshire, England.

Newton was born prematurely. His mother left him when he was three, leaving him in charge of his elderly grandmother. At the age of 16 he went to help his mother on a farm, but proved useless and was sent to prepare for Cambridge University.

From 1665 to 1666, Newton spent a lot of time away from Cambridge because of the threat of plague. At this time, Newton worked on his many ideas in optics, dynamics and mathematics that later developed into the work that he is remembered for. He returned to Cambridge in 1667 and became a fellow of Trinity College.

After extensive correspondence with Robert Hooke that started in 1679, Newton finally became interested in dynamics and he eventually formulated his solution of the planetary motion. In 1686, he published his *Principia Mathematica*.

When Newton died, he was given a national funeral and buried in Westminster Abbey.

Planck, Max Carl Ernst Ludwig (1858–1947)

Born at Kiel, Germany. Founder of the quantum theory. Although a gifted pianist, Planck decided not to study music choosing physics instead. His formulation of the equation that described black-body radiation was a triumph of mathematical reasoning. Planck was not satisfied with the introduction of the quantum to explain the equation and remained sceptical of quantum mechanics for the rest of his life.

Röntgen, William Konrad (1845–1923)

Born at Lennep, Germany.

Before he discovered X-rays, Röntgen was already regarded as one of the most outstanding experimental physicists of his day in Germany. His accidental discovery of X-rays led to him winning the first ever Nobel prize in physics in 1901.

Salam, Abdus (1926–)

Born in Jhang, Pakistan. Theoretical physicist known for unified field theories and his prediction of 'weak currents' (a type of weak interaction, like beta decay) which subsequently won him the Nobel prize in 1979. In 1964, he started to set up the International Centre for Theoretical Physics in order to help him in his work to assist physicists from developing countries.

Thomson, J.J. (1856–1940)

Born in Manchester, England. Discoverer of the electron. Thomson's discoveries relating to cathode rays and electrons was motivated by his initial view that atoms could be vortex rings in the aether – like smoke rings in air, which he had studied closely. Thomson's demonstration of the particle nature of electrons was due to the improved vacuum pump technology of the time. Previous experiments carried out by the German Heinrich Hertz had failed to show a deflection of cathode rays because the poor vacuum had left enough particles to ionise and counter the electric field set up by the plates that should have deflected the electron.

Thomson, Sir William (1824–1907)

Born in Belfast, Ireland. Made Baron Kelvin of Largs, Ayrshire in 1892.

Entered the University of Glasgow at the age of 10, became a fellow of Peterhouse College, Cambridge, at the age of 22. Thomson was knighted for his contribution to the laying of the first Atlantic cable.

Thomson worked with many scientists on theories that are the basis of modern and classical physics. He worked with Faraday on the theory of the electromagnetic field. He worked on many aspects of thermodynamics, but is mainly remembered for introducing the idea of an absolute temperature scale, the unit of which is now named after him.

Young, Thomas (1773–1829)

Born at Milverton, England. Established the wave theory of light.

Young had a remarkable memory, studied many different languages and is still remembered for his readings of Egyptian hieroglyphics, including the famous Rosetta Stone. Young started to favour a wave theory of light in the early 1800s, but had many doubts caused by his assumption that the wave motion was longitudinal. (Transverse waves were suggested some decades later by the Frenchman Augustin Fresnel.)

Yukawa, Hideki (1907–1981)

Born Hideki Ogawa in Tokyo, Japan. Devised the particle exchange theory of the nuclear force.

In 1932, Hideki married Sumi Yukawa (and by tradition took up her family's name) and became a lecturer at Osaka University. The pion, discovered in 1937, had exactly the same propertied as described in his 1935 theory that proposed a particle that carried the strong nuclear force. This finally won him the Nobel prize in 1949.

Index

absolute zero 107–8
absorbed dose 48
absorption 49–51
accelerators, particle 16–24
accidents 65–6
adiabatic expansion 103, 104, 111, 113
aether 71, 72
    and speed of light 117–19, 120
age
    of the Earth 36, 37, 38–9, 42, 43
    geological dating 41
ALEPH particle detector 22
Al-Haytham 80
alpha particles 39
    absorption of 51
    energy of 45, 50, 52, 54–5
    ionisation by 45–6
    scattering of 7–8
    tunnelling by 54–5
    see also helium
Anderson, Carl 26–7
antibaryons 33
antileptons 34, 35
antimatter see antiparticles
antineutrinos 34, 38, 53
antineutrons 28
antiparticles 26–8, 33, 34, 35
    in beta decay 38, 53
    see also particles
antiprotons 28
antiquarks 32, 33, 35
Aristotle 80
atomic mass units 11, 37
atoms
    energy levels in 92
    images of 97
    nuclear model of 7–8, 14
    nucleus of see nuclei
attenuation coefficient 51
avalanche effect 23–4

background radiation 49
baryons 35
    baryon numbers 30
    composed of quarks 32–3
Becquerel, Henri 36

beta particles
    absorption of 51
    in antimatter discovery 26–7
    emission of 38, 39
    energy of 46, 50, 53
    formation of 29–30
    ionisation by 45, 46
    see also electrons
Bhopal 65–6
Big Bang 17
binding energy 39–41, 59, 61
black-body radiation 86–7
Bohr, Niels 92
boiling 110–11, 113
    of helium 114
bombs, nuclear 62–3, 65
bosons (exchange particles) 17, 28–30
    conservation rules for 31
    types of 35
bottom (quark name) 34, 35
Boyle temperature 108, 109, 110
Boyle's law 104, 108
bubble chambers 27
butane 109

California 25
camera obscura 80
cameras 79
carbon dioxide in reactors 66
cathode rays 16, 17, 71–5
CCDs 79
centripetal force 20, 74
CERN 20, 21, 22, 24
chain reactions 62–5
charge
    charge number 30, 31, 32
    charge-mass ratio 73–5
    conservation of 30
    on electron 75–8
    fundamental charge 78
charm (quark name) 34, 35
Chernobyl 65, 66
chromatic aberration 81
circular accelerators 19–22
cloud chambers 26–7
cold, study of 106–15
colour, as quark property 35
colours, in white light 81, 83
communications 16, 70, 78
condensation 110–11, 113
conductivity see superconductivity

conservation
    of energy 101
    of mass-energy 52, 126
    rules for particles 30–4
containment 65–6, 68
control rods 64, 65, 67–8
coolant in nuclear reactors 64, 66–7, 68
cooling 107–8, 110–13
cosmic radiation 123
countercurrent heat exchanger 112–13
critical mass in fission 62–3
critical temperature of gases 109–10, 112
critical temperature of metals 114–15
criticality (in fission) 63
cryogenics 106–15
current, in superconducting materials 114, 115
cyclotrons 17, 19–20, 22

da Vinci, Leonardo 81
dating, radioactive 41–2
daughter nuclei 38, 58, 59–60, 61
de Broglie, Louis 92, 93
de Broglie relationship 9, 92
decay chain 41, 42
decay, radioactive 37–9, 41–2
    see also alpha particles; beta particles; gamma emission
decommissioning of nuclear power stations 60
density of nucleus 11–12
detectors for particles 22–4
    bubble chambers 25, 27
    cloud chambers 26–7
deuterium 67
diffraction 8, 82–3
    of electrons 8–10, 93–4
    and resolving images 92, 95
Dirac, Paul 27
dissipation see spreading, of radiation
distance, relativistic contraction of 123–5
dose equivalent 48–9
double-slit experiment 82–3, 93–4
down (quark name) 32, 35

Earth, age of 36, 37, 38–9, 42–3
Eightfold way 31–2
Einstein, Albert 6
    and the photoelectric effect 89, 90
    relativity theories of 116, 117, 119, 120
    suggests photons 87, 89, 90
electric field strength 74, 77
electric fields
    cathode rays in 72, 73–5
    in cyclotron 19–20, 22
    in electromagnetic waves 84, 86, 117
    in electron microscopes 95
    electrons in 73–8
    in Van de Graaff generator 17–18
    see also electrical forces
electrical forces
    in nuclei 12–13
      see also strong nuclear force
    on particles 74, 75, 76–8
      see also electric fields
electrical interactions 29, 35
electricity, generation by nuclear power 56–69
electromagnetic forces, photons as exchange particles for 29
electromagnetic radiation
    and atomic energy levels 90
    diffraction of 8, 82–3
    and resolving images 92, 95
    gamma rays see gamma emission
    interference of 8, 82–3
    interferometer uses 118–20
    inverse square law for 49–50
    light see light
    photons of see photons
    refraction of 81–2
    spectrum of 47, 85
    speed of see speed of light
    wave nature of 84–6, 117
    X-rays 47, 51, 85
electron microscopes 17, 91
    scanning tunnelling 97–8
    transmission 95–6
electronics, foundations for 70, 78
electrons
    antiparticle see positrons
    atomic energy levels 92
    baryon numbers 30

    as beta particles see beta particles
    cathode rays 16, 17, 71–5
    charge on 75–8
    charge-mass ratio 73–5
    collide with beta particles 46
    composed of leptons 33–4, 35
    diffraction of 8–10, 93–4
    in electric fields 73–8
    from electron guns 47
    importance to communications 70, 78
    interaction with positrons 26–8
    interference of 93–4
    in magnetic fields 73–5
    in photoelectric effect 88–9
    thermionic emission 73, 88
    tunnelling of 96–8
    wave nature of 8–10, 92–8
    see also electron microscopes; particles
electronvolt (eV) 7–8, 18, 37
electrostatic forces in nuclei 12–13
    see also strong nuclear force
energy
    of accelerated particles 18
    of alpha particles 45, 50, 52, 54–5
    atomic energy levels 92
    of beta particles 46, 50, 53
    binding 39–41, 59, 61
    in boiling 110–11, 113
    in cooling gases 107–8, 111
    electronvolt (eV) 7–8, 18, 37
    in evaporation 110–11, 113
    for exchange particles 28
    from fission 58–9, 61
    of gamma photons 50
    for gas expansion 102–3, 110
    and intensity of radiation 49
    internal see internal energy
    of ionising radiations 45–6, 48
    in isothermal expansion 103
    kinetic see kinetic energy
    mass-energy equivalence see mass-energy equivalence
    from particle annihilation 27
    in photoelectric effect 88–9
    of photons 89, 90
    potential see potential
    quantisation of 87–90
    from radioactive decay 37–9

    in refrigeration 105
    source of Sun's 39–40
    in superconductivity 114
    and temperature 100–1
    in thermionic emission 73, 88
    see also power; work
enriched fuel 62
equilibrium 99–100
equilibrium separation 13–14
ether see aether
eV (electronvolt) 7–8, 18, 37
evaporation 110–11, 113
exchange particles see bosons
exited states 52
expansion of gases 102–4
    adiabatic 103, 104, 111, 113

Faraday, Michael 71
Feynman diagrams 28–30
Feynman, Richard 28, 29
fields see electric fields; gravitational fields; magnetic fields
film transfer 113, 114
fission 58–60, 61
    chain reactions 62–5
    control rods in 64, 65, 67–8
    moderators for 63–4, 65, 67, 68
food irradiation 44–5, 46–8, 51, 55
forces
    between nucleons 12–14
    between particles 28–30
    centripetal 20, 74
    electrical see electrical forces
    electrostatic, in nuclei 12–13
    on falling objects 76, 78
    gravitational
      gravitons 29, 35
      in nuclei 12–13
    intermolecular 14
    magnetic 20
      on particles 74, 75
      see also magnetic fields
    strong nuclear see strong nuclear force
    van der Waal's 14
    see also interactions
fountain effect 114
frames of reference 118, 119, 120
    length contraction in 123–5
    speed of light in 121
    time dilation between 121–3

France, nuclear power in 56–7, 69
frequency 88–9, 90
fuel, nuclear 58–9, 62
fundamental charge 78
fundamental particles
    electron as 75
    modern view of 33, 34, 35
    search for 26–35
fusion 39–41, 59

gamma emission 38, 39
    absorption and dissipation of 50–1
    accompanies alpha emission 52
    compared to X-rays 47
    energy of 50
    inverse square law 49–50
    ionisation by 45, 46
    see also electromagnetic radiation; photons
gas-cooled reactors 66, 67
gases
    at absolute zero 107–8
    Boyle temperature 108, 109, 110
    Boyle's law for 104, 108
    cooling 111–13
    critical temperature 109–10
    expansion of 102–4
     adiabatic 103, 104, 111, 113
    ideal 102–4, 108–10, 111
    inversion temperature 112–13
    isothermal expansion 103–4
    liquefying 106, 108–10
     using Joule-Kelvin effect 111–13
    pressure of 104, 107–10
     during cooling 111–13
    real 102, 108–10, 111–13
    see also carbon dioxide; helium; hydrogen; oxygen
Geiger, Hans
    Geiger-Müller tube 23
    scattering experiment 7
Geiger-Müller tube 23
Gell-Mann, Murray 30–2
geology
    dating of rocks 41–2
    and Earth's age 36, 37, 38–9, 42, 43
    rock formation 39

gluons 35
graphite, in nuclear reactors 67
graphs 10
gravitational fields 77
gravitational forces 77
    gravitons 29, 35
    in nuclei 12–13
gravitons 29, 35

hadrons 33, 35
heat, from Earth's core 36
heat exchangers
    countercurrent heat exchanger 112–13
    in nuclear reactors 66
heavy water 67
Heisenberg's Uncertainty Principle 28
    see also probability waves
helium 40, 115
    liquefying 112
    at supercool temperatures 113–14, 115
    see also alpha particles
Hertz, Heinrich 85
high level waste 59–60, 61
high-energy experiments 16–17, 19, 24
    see also accelerators; CERN; Large Electron-Positron Collider; superconducting supercollider
historical aspects
    of communications 70, 78
    discovery of cathode rays 71–3
    physics in the 20th century 6
    theories on the age of Earth 36
    theories of light 80–9
Hooke, Robert 82
humans, effect of ionisation radiation on 45–6, 48–9
    see also food irradiation
Huygens, Christiaan 82, 83
hydrogen 112

ideal gases
    defined 102, 108
    expansion of 102–4, 111
    under pressure 108–10

images in microscopes
    in electron microscopes 96–8
    resolving 92, 95
inertial frames of reference see frames of reference
intensity, of radiation 49–51
interactions of particles
    conservation rules 30–4
    four types of 29–30, 35
interference 8, 82–3
    of electrons 93–4
    interferometer uses 118–20
interferometer 118–20
intermolecular forces 14
internal energy
    of cooling gases 107–8, 111
    in evaporation 110, 113
    in first law of thermodynamics 101
    in gas expansion 102–3
    adiabatic 103, 111
    and temperature 100–1
inverse square law 49–50
inversion temperature 112–13
ionisation by radiation 45–6, 48
    in particle detectors 22–4
ionisation chamber 22
isothermal expansion 103–4
isotopes, radioactive 18, 19, 60

Joule, James
    and Joule-Kelvin effect 111–13
    links work and energy 101
Joule-Kelvin effect 111–13

K-mesons (kaons) 30, 31, 32
kaons (K-mesons) 30, 31, 32
Kelvin, Lord 36, 37, 39
    and Joule-Kelvin effect 111–13
kelvin scale 107–8
Kepler, Johannes 80
kinetic energy
    of accelerated particles 18
    of alpha particles 45, 50, 52, 54
    of beta particles 46, 50, 53
    in electronvolt definition 7, 8, 18
    in evaporation 110
    in mass-energy equivalence 126, 127
    of photoelectrons 88–9

lambda particle 31
lambda point 113–14
Large Electron-Positron Collider (LEP) 20, 21
latent heat of vaporisation 110–11, 113
lead 38, 41–2
length contraction 123–5
lenses 81
LEP (Large Electron-Positron Collider) 20, 21
leptons 17, 33–4, 35
life on Earth 43
light 79–90
    diffraction of 8, 82–3
      and resolving images 92, 95
    interference 8, 82–3
      interferometer uses 118–20
    particle theory of 81–3, 90
    photoelectric effect 88, 89
    refraction of 81–2
    speed of see speed of light
    wave nature of 82–90
    see also electromagnetic radiation; photons
light microscopes 92, 95
linear accelerators 17, 18–19, 22
liquefying gases 106, 108–10
    using Joule-Kelvin effect 111–13
liquid drop model 14–15, 58–9
liquids
    evaporation and boiling of 110–11, 113
    helium's superfluidity 113–14
    see also liquefying gases

magnetic fields
    cathode rays in 72, 73–5
    in cyclotrons 19–20, 22
    in electromagnetic waves 84, 86
    in electron microscopes 95
    particles in 26
      electrons 73–5
    and superconductivity 115
    in synchrotrons 20–1
magnetic forces 20
    on particles 74, 75
    see also magnetic fields
magnets, superconducting 19, 22

mass
    critical mass 62–3
    loss of, in radioactive decay 37–8, 39
    mass defect 39–41
    mass-energy equivalence see mass-energy equivalence
    at speed of light 126, 127
mass-energy equivalence 18, 126–7
    and binding energy 39–41
    in fission 58–9
    in radioactive decay 37, 52
Maxwell, James Clerk 84–6, 117
medical uses
    of electron microscopes 91, 97
    for liquid oxygen 106, 110
    of particle accelerators 19
    of radionuclides 60, 61
    of superconductivity 114, 115
    of X-rays 51
Meissner levitation 106
mesons 32–3, 35
metals, critical temperature of 114–15
Michelson, Albert A. 84
    Michelson-Morley experiment 118–20
Michelson-Morley experiment 118–20
microscopes
    electron 91
      scanning tunnelling 97–8
      transmission 95–6
    light 92
Millikan, Robert
    electronic charge experiment 75–8
    photoelectric experiment 89, 90
models
    of light 90
    of the nucleus 6–15
      liquid drop model 14–15, 58–9
    of particles 33–5
moderators 63–4, 65, 67, 68
momentum
    and particle wavelength 9, 92, 95–6
    of photons 92
Moon, dating of rocks 42
Morley, E. W. 118–20
muons 34, 35, 123

negative feedback 64
neutrinos 53
    antineutrinos 34, 38, 53
    baryon numbers 30
    composed of leptons 33–4
neutrons
    antiparticle of 28
    baryon numbers 30
    composed of quarks 32, 33, 35
    conservation and decay 31, 34
    in fission 59, 60, 61
      neutron speed 62–4, 65, 67, 68
    free neutrons 48, 60, 67
    thermal 64
    see also nuclei; nucleons; particles
Newton, Isaac 81, 82
Newton's rings 82
nuclear power 56–69
nuclei
    binding energy 39–41, 59, 61
    daughter nuclei 38, 58, 59–60, 61
    decay of see radioactive decay
    density of 11–12
    diffract electrons 8–10
    fission of see fission
    forces between nucleons 12–14
      see also strong nuclear force
    fusion of 39–41, 59
    models of 6–15
      liquid drop 14–15, 58–9
    nucleon number 10–11
    radii of 7–11
    stability of 40, 41, 42, 60
    tunnelling in 54–5
    volume of 10–11
    see also nuclear power
nucleons
    forces between 12–15
    see also strong nuclear force
    nucleon number 10–11
    see also neutrons; nuclei; protons
nuclides see nuclei

optical microscopes 92, 95
orbits, electron 92
oxygen
    liquefying 112
    uses of 106, 110

pair production 28–9
    conservation rules for 31, 34
parent nucleus 38
particle accelerators 16–24
particles
    accelerating 16–24
    detectors for 22–4, 25, 26–7
    in evaporation 110, 113
    exchanging *see* bosons
    fundamental
     electron as 75
     modern view 33, 34, 35
     search for 26–35
    gas, at zero kelvin 107
    interactions of
     conservation rules 30–4
     four types of 29–30, 35
    masses 18, 35
    particle theory of light 81–3, 90
    probability waves for 94–5
    relativistic behaviour of 123, 126
    wave nature of 8–10, 92–5
    see also alpha particles; beta particles; electrons; neutrinos; neutrons; photons; protons
Pauli, Wolfgang 53
penetrating ability of ionising radiations 45, 46–7
photoelectric effect 88, 89
photons 87, 90
    as exchange particles 29, 35
    from particle annihilation 27–8
    interaction with matter 46
    momentum of 92
    in photoelectric effect 89
    speed of *see* speed of light
    see also electromagnetic radiation; gamma emission; light; X-rays
pions 35
    composition 32, 33
    conversion and conservation rules 31
    discovery 28
    evidence for existence 29
    in particle collision 29
Planck, Max 87
Planck's constant 89

Poisson, Siméon 83
Poisson spot 83
pollution
    at Bhopal 65–6
    by Chernobyl 65
    by electricity generation 69
    by nuclear power 58, 59–61, 65, 69
positrons 26–8
    composed of leptons 33–4, 35
potential energy
    between nucleons 13–14, 54
    of electron in an atom 96–7, 98
    intermolecular 14
power, defined 100
pressure, gas 104, 107–10
    in cooling gases 111–13
pressurised-water reactors (PWRs) 67
probability waves 94–5
    for electron tunnelling 96–7
    see also Heisenberg's Uncertainty Principle
protons
    antiparticle of 28
    baryon numbers 30
    composed of quarks 32, 33, 35
    conservation rules 31
    in cyclotrons 20
    emission of 38
    see also nuclei; nucleons; particles
PWRs (pressurised-water reactors) 67

Q value 38, 39, 52
quanta 87
quantum mechanics 90
    in photoelectric effect 88–9
    quanta 87
    quantum tunnelling 54–5, 96–8
    Schrödinger equation 94
    Uncertainty Principle 28
quantum tunnelling
    by alpha particles 54–5
    by electrons 96–8
quarks 17, 31–3, 34–5

radiation 44–55
    absorption of 49–51
    alpha *see* alpha particles
    background 49
    beta *see* beta particles
    black-body 86–7
    cosmic 123
    electromagnetic *see* electromagnetic radiation
    food irradiation 44–5, 46–8, 51, 55
    gamma *see* gamma emission
    intensity of 49–51
    inverse square law for 49–50
    penetrating ability of 45, 46–7
    radioactive decay 37–9, 41–2
    radioactive isotopes 18, 19, 60
    radioactivity discovered 36
    see also nuclear power
radii, of nucleus 7–11
radio waves 85
radioactive decay 37–9, 41–2
    see also alpha particles; beta particles; gamma emission
radioactive isotopes 18, 19, 60
radioactivity
    absorption of 49–51
    alpha *see* alpha particles
    beta *see* beta particles
    discovered 36
    gamma *see* gamma emission
    intensity of 49–51
    inverse square law for 49–50
    penetrating ability of 45, 46–7
    radioactive decay 37–9, 41–2
    radioactive isotopes 18, 19, 60
radioisotopes 18, 19, 60
railways 100, 101
reactors, nuclear 56–69
real gases
    adiabatic expansion of 111
    compared to ideal 102
    cooling of 111–13
    under pressure 108–10
refraction 81–2
refrigeration 105
relativity 116–27
    length contraction 123–5
    mass effects 126–7
    postulates of 120
    time dilation 121–3

resolving images 92, 95
revolutionary physics 6
    importance of theories of light 79
    particles act as waves 8
    relativity as 116
    in telecommunications 70
Röntgen, William 85

Salam, Abdus 29
scanning tunnelling electron microscope 97–8
scattering, of alpha particles 7–8
Schrödinger equation 94
semiconductor particle detector 23
simple accelerators 17–19
size, of nucleus 7–11
SLAC (Stanford Linear Accelerator) 18
solid state particle detector 23
spark chamber 24
spark counter 23–4
Special Relativity see relativity
specific latent heat of vaporisation 110–11, 113
spectra
    of beta energy 53
    electromagnetic 47, 85
speed, of neutrons 62–4, 65, 67, 68
speed of light 116–22, 125–6
    mass at 126, 127
    Maxwell's value 84
    Michelson measures 84
    Michelson-Morley experiment 118–20
    particles close to 20, 22
    and time dilation 121–3
    as universal constant 85–6
    see also relativity
spreading, of radiation 49–50
SSC (superconducting supercollider) 16, 24
stability, of nuclei 40, 41, 42, 60
standing waves 92–3
Stanford Linear Accelerator (SLAC) 18
steam engines 99–100, 101
STM (scanning tunnelling electron microscope) 97–8
Stokes' law 76, 78
stopping voltage 89
strange (quark name) 32, 35

strangeness 30–1, 32
strong nuclear force 12, 13–14, 28–9
    acts on alpha particles 54
    boson for 35
    see also interactions
sublimation 109
Sun's energy 39–40
superconducting magnets 19, 22
superconducting supercollider (SSC) 16, 24
superconductivity 106, 114–15
supercool temperatures 113–15
superfluidity 113–14
synchrotrons 17, 20–2

taus 17, 34, 35
technology
    of communications 70, 78
    importance of light to 79
    relationship with science 99, 105
telegraph 70
television 79, 95
    relativity in 123, 126
TEM (transmission electron microscopes) 95–6
temperature
    absolute zero 107–8
    in adiabatic expansion 103, 111
    and black-body radiation 86–7
    Boyle temperature 108, 109, 110
    cooling of gases 111–13
    critical temperature of gases 109–10
    critical temperature of metals 114–15
    and energy 100–1
    inversion temperature 112–13
    in isothermal expansion 103, 104
    low 106–15
    supercool 113–15
    and thermal equilibrium 100
terminal velocity 76, 78
thermal equilibrium 100
thermal neutrons 64
thermal transfer 100
thermionic emission 73, 88

thermodynamics 99–105
    adiabatic expansion 103, 104, 111, 113
    cooling 107–8, 110–13
    first law of 101, 102–3
    isothermal expansion 103–4
    of refrigeration 105
Thomson, George 93
Thomson, J. J. 16, 72–5
Thomson, Sir William see Kelvin, Lord
Three Mile Island 66
threshold frequency 88
time, relativistic approach 116, 120–6
time dilation 121–3
top (quark name) 34, 35
transmission electron microscopes (TEM) 95–6
tunnelling
    by alpha particles 54–5
    by electrons 96–8
TV 79, 95
    relativity in 123, 126

ultraviolet catastrophe 86–7
Uncertainty Principle 28
up (quark name) 32, 35
uranium 62
    decay of 38
    in fission 58–9, 61, 62–5
    for geological dating 41–2
    hazards of mining 69

Van de Graaff generator 17–18
van der Waal's forces 14
vaporisation 110–11, 113
viscosity 113–14
viscous drag 76, 78
volume
    in isothermal expansion 104
    of nuclei 10–11
    pressure and volume of gases 108–10

waste, nuclear 58, 59–61, 69
water in nuclear reactors 67
water-cooled reactors 67
Watt, James 99–100
wave-particle duality 8–10

wavelength, of particles 9, 92, 95–6
waves
    electromagnetic 84–6, 117
    see also electromagnetic
    radiation
    probability 94–5
    standing waves 92–3
    in theory of light 82–90
    wave nature of particles 8–10,
    92–8
weak interaction 29–30, 35
Weinberg, Stephen 29
work
    by expanding gases 102, 104,
    111–13
    defined 100
    in refrigeration 105
    and thermal energy transfer
    101
World-Wide Web 24

X-rays 47
    discovery of 85
    medical uses 51
    see also electromagnetic
    radiation; photons

young Earth theory 36, 37, 39
Young, Thomas 82–3
Yukawa, Hideki 28